TARGET FOR TOMORROW

Space Travel of the Future

Dr. I. M. LEVITT

Director, Fels Planetarium of the Franklin Institute

Target
for Tomorrow

SPACE TRAVEL OF THE FUTURE

Fleet Publishing Corporation,

New York

LIBRARY OF CONGRESS CATALOG CARD NUMBER: 59-8929

PRINTED IN THE UNITED STATES OF AMERICA

To
PETER AND NANCY
to whom—with their friends—
the space age belongs.

Contents

Contents

Preface

FOR EIGHT YEARS I have been writing a syndicated newspaper column on space travel under the title of "Wonders of the Universe." In my search for material I have traveled extensively both in this country and abroad, speaking to the leaders of the new science and reporting fresh developments from the field, the laboratory, and from industry. I have watched the space travel panorama as it progressed from ridicule to respectability, and from reluctant acceptance to today's world-wide enthusiasm as the most impressive and promising force to appear on the science horizon. During all this time the most recent concepts in the field were interpreted in this column and aimed straight at the layman.

It was repeatedly urged that the most provocative

of these columns should be made available in book form. To this I agreed only on condition that opportunity be given to bring the columns up to date, and that the second half of the work be entirely new material on which we had been working for some time. Fortunately, the very development of the American Man-in-Space and other startling programs has paralleled these efforts. The logic of presenting the whole story at this time impressed George Little, Editor of General Features Corporation, and it was at his insistence that the manuscript was finished and sent to the publisher.

In my dealings with the great and near-great in the realm of astronautics I have had the good fortune to be with many of them when big things were in the making. Lucky timing, maybe—but I have worked diligently for it.

In all phases of the writing and publishing of this book, luck and timing have been with me. The velocity of progress in world astronautics at this moment seems likely to make credible, even to conservatives, the carefully wrought ideas which only months ago would have been deemed wild conjecture.

The book is roughly divided into two sections. The first deals with what is already known and what we are doing to further develop the science of space travel. The second is dedicated to the future. In the latter section may be found what I consider to be the most stimulating aspects of the entire field.

When we project into the future we see spectacular developments cascading into place to point the way to things to come. The various chapters pursue the question of new propulsion systems, the conquest of the moon, the establishment of a closed ecological cycle on the moon, the moon as a point of take-off for travel to the planets, and also as the launching site for a celestial Noah's Ark which will take man beyond the solar system and to the stars in interstellar space. Finally, the possibility of traveling at relativistic speeds is discussed. This I find one of the most stimulating facets of science.

There is added an appendix concerning the training needed for careers in astronautics. Thousands of letters have been received from youngsters seeking guidance in the selection of subjects of study in this great new field. My views on how youth may prepare are here given. While some may disagree with the specific content of the appendix, none will dispute the necessity for an educational guide in this area of national endeavor.

In this undertaking I have had the benefit of the advice of many prominent men in the field. To Darrell Romick, Bob Haviland, Fred Singer, Kurt Stehling, John Streeter, and Roy Marshall I want to extend my sincere thanks.

The Fels Planetarium
Philadelphia, Pa.

I. M. LEVITT

Introduction

IN THE EARLY DAYS of 1951, more than seven years before Sputnik, I went to Philadelphia to visit the author and discuss the possibility of having him write a column on space travel. When I first met Dr. Levitt in his impressive setting behind the planetarium console talking about the planets, space travel, and satellites, I felt that if only he could capture in the written word the then seemingly impossible but scientifically plausible things we discussed, the column would, indeed, be popular with newspaper readers all over the world.

Dr. Levitt's work was brought to my attention through a monthly astronomical article he was writing for the *Newark News*. And from my inquiries I became aware of his academic achievements, his success as an educator, and his reputation as director of the world-famous Fels Planetarium. These qualities I deemed important to pioneer thinking and influence action on space travel.

Then came "Wonders of the Universe"—a Sunday newspaper feature now starting its eighth year. In the early days we thought it might be best if the feature dealt with all phases of science because the public did not seem ready to believe the fantastic stories of space travel.

The column had a modest beginning with only a few newspapers. But soon its acceptance by editors began to expand, and in a few years it was being translated into other languages and carried by newspapers in many nations of the free world.

From a readership of perhaps one million in 1952, the column is now read by nearly eighty million people every week. This increase has come because some of the most astute men on the contemporary scene— newspaper editors—see in Dr. Levitt the spokesman for the space age. Every age has its prophet, and he is a major prophet on satellites and space travel.

Dr. Levitt's repeated appearances on radio, television, and before large audiences throughout the country are founded on his remarkable ability to give the layman a glimpse of the future in understandable language. More than that, he succeeds in giving readers a unique feeling of participation in these great scientific developments.

Here, in TARGET FOR TOMORROW—Space Travel of the Future—Dr. Levitt uses the sum of his background and experience to set forth in full book form the most challenging and yet heartening projection of man's future in space. If I may venture a prediction of my own, this account, this blueprint if you will, of the prospect of extraterrestrial human activity will long rank as one of the brilliant intellectual contributions of the rocket era.

S. GEORGE LITTLE
Executive Editor
General Features Corporation

TARGET FOR TOMORROW
Space Travel of the Future

CHAPTER 1

Our Home in Space

Since man's earliest days he has raised his eyes to the stars and has wondered what is "out there." With the invention and immediate astronomical use of the telescope, early in the 17th century, our knowledge began to increase by leaps and bounds. But where does "out there" really begin?

Except for a few thousand feet from the earth's surface at sea level to the tops of mountains, we were for a long time handicapped in our efforts to learn by actual sampling anything about the space above our heads. Our atmosphere is a deep, turbulent, and mysterious ocean through which the light from distant objects must come before we can perceive and analyze it. In 1783, the brothers Montgolfier in France sent some animals aloft a few hundred feet in a smoke-filled balloon. In 1956, the experimental Bell aircraft X-2 carried a man to a height of 126,000 feet, almost 24 miles—the greatest reach, so far, of man himself into space.

Rockets and artificial satellites now have probed to far greater heights and, sometimes slowly, sometimes swiftly, our knowledge of space and of our place in it is increasing. So far, man himself continues to be earth-bound, but that he will eventually and inevitably be able to leave the earth to set foot on other bodies in the universe is a thought that cannot seriously be challenged.

What is the earth, that is not only man's home but also the planet on which he has evolved—the planet that has shaped and conditioned him? Until now, at least half of the research projects of high altitude rockets and satellites have been devoted to study of the earth, and we can do no better than to examine what we know about our taking-off base for the exploration of space.

The earth is the third planet outward from the sun. Nearer the sun are Mercury and Venus. Beyond the earth lie Mars, Jupiter, Saturn, Uranus, Neptune, and Pluto. Pluto's distance from the sun is 102 times that of Mercury; the earth's is about 2.6 times that of the innermost planet.

Measurements of distances in the universe depend essentially upon the methods of the surveyor. As the surveyor can make observations of a distant point from the two ends of a measured base line and thus determine the distance of the point, so astronomers from two points on the earth can observe an object such as the moon and determine its distance.

To determine the distance of the sun directly by this method would be impossible, because the longest base line available, the diameter of the earth, is much too small for accurate observations to determine such a great distance. However, as we shall see in the next chapter, we can determine the relative positions in space of the sun, the earth, and a third body such as another planet. Then, if the other planet is close enough for its distance to be measured by the surveyor's method, we can determine the distance of the sun.

One of the so-called minor planets or asteroids, named Eros, approaches the earth to within 15,000,000 miles. We can measure this distance. We know the ratio of the sun's distance to the asteroid's distance at any moment, so we can then determine the sun's distance from the earth.

In 1931, a near approach of Eros permitted a new determination and a slightly improved value of 93,000,000 miles as the sun-earth distance. This is the fundamental base line for measurement of all other distances in the universe. Light, traveling at a velocity of about 186,300 miles per second, requires 8 minutes $18\frac{1}{2}$ seconds to reach us from the sun.

The earth's orbit around the sun is very nearly circular, so nearly so that it is very difficult to draw it as other than a circle; yet it is really an ellipse and we are closest to the sun about January 3, farthest from it about July 5. The difference between these extreme distances is a trifle over 3,100,000 miles— only a thirtieth of the average distance.

Because this variation is so small, and because we are closest to the sun in January and farthest from it in July, it should be obvious that this changing distance of the earth from the sun can not be responsible for the seasonal changes on earth. These changes are brought about by the fact that the earth's equator is tilted by 23½ degrees to the plane of the earth's path around the sun.

As the earth revolves around the sun in the period of a year, and rotates on its axis once a day, the axis remains parallel to itself; so in January the northern hemisphere is tilted away from the sun, the southern hemisphere toward the sun. The weather is cold up north and warm below the equator. In July, the reverse is true and in the northern hemisphere the weather is warm because that hemisphere is then tilted toward the sun and the sun rides high in the sky.

The sun's radiations affect the earth intimately. We seldom realize how much, because we think only in terms of the sun's light and heat. All our wind, rain, and other weather phenomena are produced by the sun. The sun's ultraviolet radiation produces effects in our high atmosphere that literally make life possible on the surface. Radiations and particles from the sun affect radio transmission and the strength and direction of the earth's magnetic field.

We may begin our study of the earth by saying that it can be roughly divided into atmosphere, lithosphere, and hydrosphere. Suppose we think first of the lithosphere, the solid portion of the earth—literally, the sphere of rock.

The lithosphere constitutes most of the bulk of the earth, although only about five-sevenths of its surface shows above the hydrosphere, the ocean cover. Because of the rotation of the earth each 24 hours, the lithosphere is not exactly spherical. Its shape is what we call an oblate spheroid, somewhat flattened at the poles. According to figures adopted in 1924, the polar diameter is 7900.02 miles; the mean equatorial diameter is 7926.70 miles. These dimensions apply to mean sea level.

The deepest trough in the oceans is 35,700 feet below sea level; Mount Everest's peak rises to about 29,000 feet above the sea. Sometimes we feel that these irregularities of the earth's crust make our planet a rather rough ball, but suppose we think of the earth as reduced to only 10 inches in diameter. The polar flattening of the earth amounts to only 13.34 miles either way from an average value of 7913.36 miles. Reduced to the scale of a 10-inch ball, this would be a deviation of only one-sixtieth of an inch—about three or four times the thickness of a human hair. The ocean troughs and high mountains would introduce little wrinkles of less than a hundredth of an inch here and there. That 10-inch ball would roll almost as smoothly as a bowling ball.

We can explore fairly well the surface of the lithosphere, even that portion at great depths below the surface of the seas. Roughly we can divide the materials we find into three categories: igneous, sedimentary, and crystalline. The first are those materials that reveal that there has been volcanic activity in the past and present. The second are those that reveal that materials have been deposited at the bottoms of seas and lakes. The third are of a type well described by the name. In addition to these there are the conglomerates—mixtures cemented together by natural actions of water and chemicals of various kinds.

We can probe directly into the earth's crust in mines, the deepest being about two miles, and by means of drill cores of wells, the deepest extending to about five miles. On the average, we find the mountains to consist largely of a material we call *sial*, a coined word indicating that these rocks are made up chiefly of compounds of silicon and aluminum with other elements. These rocks are comparatively light in weight and color, more so than the heavier and darker rocks known as *sima*—compounds of silicon and magnesium with other elements, that underlie the ocean sediments. Granite is the chief sialic rock, therefore we say that the continents are granitic. Basalt is the chief simatic rock, so we refer to the ocean basins as basaltic.

Below the sima is the interior of the earth, consisting (at least in its upper levels, just below the crust) of denser non-crystalline rock. Most of the crust—only about 20 to 30 miles thick—and all of the remaining interior of the earth have been probed only by means of seismographs, the instruments that detect and analyze waves from earthquakes. The great Assam quake of August, 1950, released about 100,000 times as much energy as an atomic bomb, and this energy was in great portion dissipated in sending waves all over and through the earth. Seismographs picked up the waves at hundreds of stations. From such quakes we can learn much of what lies below us.

At the crust, the density of the rocks is about $3\frac{1}{2}$ times that of water. At a depth of 1800 miles, the density is about $5\frac{1}{2}$ times water. There the density suddenly jumps to about $9\frac{1}{2}$ times water and increases to about $11\frac{1}{2}$ times water at a depth of 3000 miles. At the center of the earth, about 3960 miles down, the density is between $14\frac{1}{2}$ and 18 times that of water—denser than mercury but not as dense as gold.

The temperature increases as we go deeper into

the earth. In deep mines the temperature rises at the rate of about 54° F. per mile of descent, but we are rather sure that such a rapid rate of increase does not continue all the way to the center. Present estimates of the central temperature range between 3600° F. and 11,500° F.—a wide range to be sure, but one to be expected when we consider the difficulties involved in the determination.

Much of the earth's mantle below the crust consists of materials with the characteristics of magnesium-iron silicates. There are materials similar to olivine and to silica, magnesia, and iron oxides farther down. It is notable that we find these materials in meteorites, the objects that fall to earth from outside, originating, we believe today, from the disruption of a planet millions of years ago. The core of the earth is believed to consist of nickel-iron, the same material that composes the iron meteorites and is found sprinkled in small grains throughout the stony meteorites.

While there remains much controversy in these matters, the consensus is that from 1800 to 3000 miles down the core is liquid, while from 3000 miles to the center the core is solid, despite the high temperature, because there the pressure is of the order of 25,000 tons per square inch.

The earth has a magnetic field that, at the surface, is complicated apparently by local effects. The north magnetic pole measured at the earth's surface is at the tip of North America, north and to the west of Hudson Bay; the south magnetic pole is near the coast of Antarctica, south of the east coast of Australia.

From observations of more than 400 years we know that the earth's magnetic field changes in strength and direction. Modern experts believe that there is a fundamental magnetic field that remains always lined up with the earth's axis of rotation. Superimposed on this is a residual magnetic field in which occur the changes that we observe. Through the centuries of observation this residual field has been drifting westward at such a rate that it will make a complete trip around the earth in about 1600 years —a remarkably short period of time.

Geologists find natural magnetic materials, such as magnetite and hematite, buried in the rocks. At various levels, as in the Grand Canyon or other deep gorges, these materials are lined up in different directions. The interpretation is that the earth's magnetic field has changed its direction continuously because the earth's axis of rotation has wandered on the surface of the globe. If this is correct, the north end of the earth's axis was off the coast of Washington 600 million years ago, in mid-Pacific 500 million years ago, and in Mongolia about 250 million years ago. We must not interpret this as a change of position of the earth's axis, itself; rather, we must think of the earth as slipping with respect to a fixed axis.

More than a century ago it was shown that the earth's magnetic field must originate inside the earth, but only as recently as 1939 was a mechanism suggested. Motions of material in a fluid core of the earth could set up electrical fields which, in turn, would produce magnetic fields throughout the earth. Too complicated to detail here, this theory is believed today to be the correct one. Further, because the core may not always be rotating exactly as the earth's surface is, the magnetic field can be expected to change.

One finding from explorations at high altitudes in balloons and rockets is that when we get away from the surface the magnetic poles are in different locations and are more nearly exactly opposite each other. As measured out in space, the earth's north magnetic pole is nearer Greenland.

By far the most important part of the earth as far as space travel is concerned is the atmosphere. It is a rather intriguing fact that though we know the total weight of the atmosphere, we do not know its volume. A column of air one inch on a side, extending from the surface of the earth to the "top" of the atmosphere, weighs 14.7 pounds, on the average. When we multiply this normal atmospheric pressure by the number of square inches of the earth's surface, we obtain the total weight of the atmosphere—5,800,000,000,000,000 tons. We do not know the volume, however, because we do not know exactly how high lies the level that we should call the "top" of the atmosphere.

Today we recognize several approximately defined layers. So much confusion exists in the terminology of the various atmospheric shells that for our purpose we shall use that employed by the Air Force Geophysics Directorate in Cambridge, Mass. Various agencies derive different temperatures in their models depending on the assumptions made as to the compositions of the layers and the state of the gases, whether molecular or atomic.

The shell closest to the surface of the earth, the *troposphere,* contains about 75% of the mass of the atmosphere. In it our weather is generated; we may consider the troposphere as a great weather machine powered by the sun. At sea level there are about 400 million million million molecules of air in each cubic inch. They are so closely packed that each particle soon collides with another. We call the average distance between collisions the "mean free path," and at sea level it is about a millionth of an inch.

The troposphere varies in thickness from about five miles at the poles to about 12 miles at the equator. The heating of the earth's surface by the sun causes turbulence in it. Coupled with this solar heating effect is the rotation of the earth, and together they produce the general air currents, the winds, rain, snow, sleet, hail, and other aspects of the weather.

From the surface of the earth to the *tropopause,* the top of the troposphere, the temperature falls more or less steadily from about 65° F. above zero to a cold 40° F. below.

Above the tropopause is the *stratosphere,* extending up to an uncertain 20 miles above the earth's surface. In it the temperature declines from 40° F. below zero to 85° F. below, at a height of about 12 miles, then curiously rises to about 35° F. below zero at the *stratopause,* the top of this layer. In the lower region of the stratosphere are the recently discovered strong air currents of high velocity—the jet streams. The threadlike cirrus clouds, formed of ice crystals, are in the stratosphere, as are also the strange, mysterious "mother-of-pearl" clouds whose origin and composition are unknown.

Above the stratopause, at an altitude of 20 miles, the *chemosphere* extends to a height of 50 miles. Here the temperature first rises from 35° F. below zero to about 30° F. above, at a height of 30 miles. Then it once more declines to 90° F. below zero at the *chemopause,* 50 miles high.

The chemosphere is an enormous photochemical laboratory in which the sun's ultraviolet radiation produces strange chemical reactions in the atmospheric molecules. This radiation produces ozone from oxygen and also breaks up the ozone to prevent a too-thick layer. Without ozone in our atmosphere, too much ultraviolet would reach the surface of the earth and life would be strangely different, if not quite impossible. As ozone possesses the property of absorbing heat from solar radiation, the increase in temperature in the high stratosphere and low chemosphere is accounted for. It is in the chemosphere that most of the meteors burn out.

Above the chemopause, and extending to a height of 250 miles, we find the *ionosphere* which, despite its great height, has been extensively studied. Auroral displays—the northern and southern lights—are found extending from almost the bottom of this layer all the way up through it and beyond. These are produced as charged particles ejected by the sun reach the atmosphere and get tangled with the earth's magnetic field. This explains why the aurora is stronger deep north and deep south on the earth, for there the lines of force of the magnetic field are closer together. In the ionosphere, at heights of 60 to 120 miles, still other radiations or charged particles (or both) coming from the sun, produce the recently discovered infrared and green airglow. Molecules of sodium, oxygen, and a combination of oxygen and hydrogen are excited by these emanations from the sun and emit a glow invisible to the eye.

The temperature in the ionosphere rises continuously from 90° F. below zero to about 350° F. above, at a height of 120 miles. From that point on, the temperature continues to rise to many hundreds of degrees at the *ionopause,* 250 miles high. But we must be careful not to interpret this temperature in terms of heat, because temperature is really only a measure of how fast the particles travel. We have already seen that at the surface of the earth the molecules of the air are crowded, and collide with each other so frequently that they don't have a chance to get up much speed. But the mean free path at a height of 70 miles is about 51 inches; at 140 miles it is about 3,600 feet; at 250 miles, the top of the ionosphere, particles travel 43 miles before they collide with another. They travel fast, but because there are so few of them they produce no sensation of heat as we understand it.

In the ionosphere are the layers of electrons that provide reflecting layers for radio waves. Without these layers, it would be impossible to get radio signals beyond the horizon. We owe these layers to the sun's ultraviolet radiation, which chips electrons from some of the molecules of the air.

The D layer, the lowest one, is probably actually in the chemosphere, or at best very low in the ionosphere. It reflects long waves with frequencies of from 10 to 500 kilocycles per second but lets shorter waves pass through. The E layer lies at an average height of about 75 miles and reflects the broadcast bands. The F_1 layer averages 120 miles in altitude and reflects regular short-wave signals; the F_2 layer is more than 150 miles high and reflects still shorter waves. Still another uncertain electron stratum, the

G layer, lies above the ionosphere. Television and FM radio waves, much shorter still, are normally not reflected by any of these layers.

Changes occur in the layers, both in heights and in electron density, so their characteristics are under intense investigation almost constantly. We know they are formed by solar ultraviolet and X-ray waves because the time of day, the season of the year, the latitude of the observer, and the condition of the sun's activity all produce changes. Sometimes, inexplicably, there appear to be denser clouds of electrons here and there in these layers, and then even TV and FM signals will be reflected and programs will be picked up from great distances.

Above the ionopause at a height of 250 miles the *mesosphere* begins, and extends to about 600 miles. This is a region that only man-made satellites can explore. So few particles exist there that, except in the lowest level, there are too few electrons to form reflecting layers for radio waves. But auroral displays are formed in this layer, as well as in the ionosphere below. Only a few billion molecules per cubic inch are necessary, however, for such displays.

Beyond the *mesopause* lies the *exosphere*—outer space. Somewhere about 600 to 625 miles high, the particle density has become so low that collisions occur so seldom that particles of the earth's atmosphere can escape into space. Here, perhaps, is what we can call the "top" of the atmosphere.

It is rather notable that not one of the first seven man-made satellites—four American, three Russian—had its lowest altitude in the exosphere; so we can say that each of them dipped into our atmosphere. We shall be able to discover more about the mesosphere and the ionosphere from these satellites and from the rate at which they are brought to earth by friction with these tenuous layers. Barring a catastrophe such as a collision with a large meteorite, a satellite in an orbit with the lowest point at somewhere beyond, say, 750 miles should revolve around the earth for many thousands of years.

CHAPTER 2

Motions in the Sky

Everyone knows that the sun rises in the east, stands highest in the sky at noon, and sets in the west. Comparatively few can as positively assert from their own observations that everything else in the heavens behaves in the same way—moving westward across the sky—although we have all been taught that the earth rotates on its axis.

It is the earth's rotation from west to east that produces this east to west motion in the sky. It is only an apparent motion; as the rotating earth carries us eastward under the sun, moon, planets, and stars, these celestial objects appear to move westward over us. Until man learned that the earth is rotating, he was hard put to it to explain any motion in the heavens.

Even today it is difficult to understand how a rotating earth can feel so firm, fixed, and immutable beneath our feet; yet there are many proofs of the earth's rotation. In 1851, the French scientist Foucault hung a heavy ball on a long wire suspended from the apex of the dome of the Pantheon in Paris. As this great pendulum swung majestically to and fro, the direction in which it traced out its path seemed continuously to change. The plane of swing of the pendulum was not itself changing with respect to the floor; the floor was slowly rotating because the south edge of it, nearer the equator, must travel faster than the north edge as the earth rotates. In the northern hemisphere, such a pendulum free to swing in any direction appears to change its swing in the clockwise direction; in the southern hemisphere, the change is in a counter-clockwise direction.

Motions of winds, trajectories of artillery shells, and many other phenomena prove indisputably that the earth rotates, and we can time this motion accurately by observation of the stars. We know even that sometimes the earth's rotation gradually slows down by tiny fractions of a second for a few years, then speeds up again, probably because of motion and redistribution of material in the massive core of the earth. Today we can make clocks that depend on the vibrations of crystals or release of nuclear particles from atoms, and these are more regular in their operation than the rotation of the earth which has been our fundamental mechanism for keeping time.

When we wish to investigate motions in the sky we first choose as our plane of reference the horizon. The point exactly overhead is called the zenith, and we say that the altitude of the zenith is 90 degrees. If an object is halfway up the sky from the horizon to the zenith, its altitude is 45 degrees, a third of the way up 30 degrees, and so on. So we have one measure of, say, a star's position in the sky. We call it altitude, and it is measured in degrees of arc.

We need another measure as well—the direction. We call this azimuth and we measure it along the horizon, beginning with zero at the north point. We then count off along the horizon toward the east; the exact east point has an azimuth of 90 degrees. On we go to the south point whose azimuth is 180 degrees, and on to the west point where the azimuth is 270 degrees. Beyond the west point we approach the north point where the azimuth is 360 degrees or zero degrees.

To be precise, we imagine a line drawn on the sky from the zenith through the object and on down to the horizon. We call this a vertical circle. The altitude of the object is the angular distance measured along the vertical circle from the horizon to the object. The azimuth of the object is the azimuth of the point where the vertical circle cuts the horizon.

Now, suppose we think of the sun's motion across the sky on March 21 or September 23, for a place

halfway up in the northern hemisphere of the earth
—a latitude of 45 degrees north. At sunrise, the sun's
altitude is zero (it is then on the horizon) and its
azimuth is 90 degrees (it rises exactly at the east
point on these two days of the year). The altitude
and azimuth both increase until noon when the sun
is 45 degrees high in the south—altitude 45 degrees,
azimuth 180 degrees. At sunset, after the azimuth
has been steadily increasing and the altitude has
been decreasing, the altitude is again zero, the azimuth is 270 degrees.

Between March 21 and September 23, the sun
rises north of east—its azimuth is between zero and
90 degrees at sunrise. It stands higher than 45 degrees at noon, but its azimuth then is still 180 degrees. It sets north of west, so its azimuth then is
between 270 and 360 degrees, and the altitude is
again zero.

Between September 23 and March 21, the sun
rises south of east, sets south of west, and at noon
stands lower than 45 degrees, for this place that we
have used throughout our example.

So we can describe the motion of the sun or any
other object in the sky as the earth turns, by tabulat-
ing its altitude and azimuth against time. But this
is not the object's path in space, because these positions have been referred to a particular place on the
earth. As soon as we observe the same object from
another place, these figures all change. We must

devise some system of coördinates that will apply for any place, or that can be transformed into altitude and azimuth for any place.

This time we choose as our fundamental plane that of the celestial equator, exactly above the equator of the earth. We have also the north and south celestial poles, exactly above the earth's corresponding poles. In our altazimuth system, there was a different horizon for every observer, but there is only one celestial equator that applies to all observers; so we have now got started on a system that is general, not personal.

We imagine lines that pass from the north celestial pole across the celestial equator to the south celestial pole. We call these hour circles. When you examine a globe of the earth, you will find lines that run from the north pole to the south pole, cutting the equator at right angles. We call these meridians of longitude, and our hour circles in the sky are just like meridians of longitude. On earth, we pick out one of these meridians, the one passing through Greenwich, England, and we use this as our starting point for measuring longitude, both east and west, from Greenwich. In the sky, we pick out a certain hour circle as a starting point for measuring what we call right ascension, which is the analogue of longitude on the earth.

The vernal equinox is the point in the sky where the sun crosses the celestial equator moving from south to north, on March 21. The hour circle passing through the vernal equinox is the one we choose for our starting point. But right ascension is measured only eastward from this hour circle, all the way around through 360 degrees, instead of 180 degrees east or west, as with longitude. And, instead of degrees, we usually use units of time—hours, minutes, seconds—to indicate right ascension, 24 hours being equivalent of 360 degrees. Thus, each hour is equal to 15 degrees, each minute of time equal to 15 minutes of arc, and so on.

Now we need another coördinate, and this one is exactly like latitude on the earth, which is the angular distance of a place north or south of the earth's equator. In the heavens we use the celestial equator, of course, and we call the measure declination instead of latitude. An object on the celestial equator has a declination of zero degrees and, as the earth turns, the object appears to travel exactly above the earth's equator. An object 30 degrees north of the celestial equator has a declination of 30 degrees north, one 45 degrees south of the celestial equator has a declination of 45 degrees south, and so on. The celestial poles have declinations of exactly 90 degrees.

We can tabulate the right ascensions and declinations of the stars in catalogues. Because of the rather elementary geometry involved, an observer can easily calculate the azimuth and altitude of any star for his place and for any given time of observation. In this way, we do not need to tabulate the azimuths and altitudes for all stars for all places on earth and for all possible times—an obviously impossible task.

It could be inferred from what has just been detailed that the right ascension and declination of a star remain forever constant. This is not true, but the corrections are progressive and are easily applied. We can still tabulate the right ascensions and declinations of stars for a given instant or epoch, then apply the corrections for any other desired instant.

There are essentially three corrections to be applied, one of them owing to the fact that the stars themselves are slowly moving with respect to each other. After very precise observations of a star's positions at various times, we can tabulate this so-called "proper motion" so that allowance can always be made for it.

The other two corrections are due to gravitational interactions of the sun, earth, and moon. The earth's equator is tilted by 23½ degrees to the plane of the earth's orbit or path around the sun. If the earth were a perfect sphere, the axis of rotation of the earth would remain precisely parallel to itself at all times; but, as we learned in the preceding chapter, the earth has an equatorial bulge. It is like a spinning gyroscopic top with a heavy rim. Any top here on earth, unless it is spinning with its axis exactly vertical, performs a wobbling motion with its axis pointing in various directions, sweeping out a figure like an ice cream cone because the earth is pulling up the top and the top resists this attempt.

We call this phenomenon *precession,* and it applies to the spinning earth as well. As the earth revolves around the sun, the sun pulls on the equatorial bulge, trying to straighten up the axis of the earth so that the earth's equator will lie exactly in the plane of the earth's orbit. The earth's gyroscopic action is opposed to this attempt and, as a result, precession occurs. The earth's axis slowly changes its direction, so that the north celestial pole is steadily progressing among the stars. This is a rather slow progression, however; in about 25,800 years the earth's axis traces out a circle 47 degrees in diameter among the stars and returns to its previous position.

Because the right ascensions and declinations of the stars are based on the positions of the celestial equator and the celestial poles among the stars, these coördinates must be slowly changing. But we know the rate and the direction, so we can make allowance for precession.

The moon's orbit with respect to the earth is precessing, too, because it is tilted by about five degrees to the earth's orbit. As the moon's orbit precesses, the moon's pull on the earth's equatorial bulge produces a nodding, or *nutation,* of the earth's axis. This is small, but is taken into consideration in precise work. It has a period of 19 years. If you spin a big top very rapidly, you can see precession as the axis swings around in a circle. If you flick the end of the axis with a finger, another faster wiggle appears and this corresponds to nutation.

Here we have introduced gravitation, a strange universal property of all matter. In early days, there was much speculation about the fact that objects fall to the earth's surface if released. Not until less than three centuries ago was this phenomenon formalized by the great English scientist Isaac Newton. Even now we do not know what gravitation is; we recognize it as a property of matter, we can describe its action, but we feel a little uneasy about it in several ways. For example, is gravitation instantaneous, or is it propagated with a certain speed? Suppose an object is traveling away from the earth at very high speed. At every instant there must be a certain gravitational pull between the earth and the object, but can we calculate that pull for a particular position of the object without allowing for the possibility that gravitation is a wave phenomenon, somewhat like light, that travels fast but definitely at a finite speed?

Perhaps we shall be able to devise experiments or make crucial observations to decide this question, but today we can at least say that we can make pretty accurate observations and predictions of motion by assuming gravitation to be instantaneous, and a general property of all matter, depending only on mass and not at all on composition or size.

There is no place in the universe where the earth's gravitational pull is zero. We can only find places where another gravitational pull is greater, perhaps to the point that the earth's is entirely negligible as compared with the new one.

Isaac Newton in 1687 stated the law of gravitation: Every particle of matter in the universe attracts every other particle, with a force that depends on the product of their masses and is inversely proportional to the square of the distance between them.

Suppose we have two bodies of exactly the same mass, separated by a certain distance. The attraction between them will be a certain amount that can be calculated by the equation Newton gave us. If we leave them the same distance apart, but double the mass of one of them, the attraction now is double the original value. If we double the masses of both bodies, the attraction becomes four times what it was originally. The force depends on the product of the masses.

Suppose we again have the two original bodies, but we double the distance between them; the attraction now is one-fourth of what it was. If we triple the distance, the attraction is only one-ninth of the original. The force is inversely proportional to the square of the distance—the distance multiplied by itself.

Newton's announcement of the law of gravitation was delayed for many years by details and the lack of mathematical tools to attack the problem. Not until he had invented a new branch of mathematics, called the calculus, was he able to feel that we can sum up every particle of the earth combined, so that we can consider the earth's gravitational force for bodies outside to be concentrated at the earth's center. When he was able to do this, he could prove that the moon is falling toward the center of the earth—the rate is one-twentieth of an inch per half mile of orbit—in a way exactly consistent with the rate of fall of an apple or other object near the earth's surface.

Newton's other great contribution in this field of dynamics was his statement of the laws of motion, earlier intuitively sensed by the great Italian, Galileo. The essentials can be summed up thus: Every body continues in its state of rest or motion in a straight line unless it is acted upon by some outside force. If another force is applied, the body's change of motion will be in the direction of that force and the deviation will be proportional to the force.

If the moon were alone in the universe, it would remain at rest or would travel in a straight line. But the earth disturbs the moon, and the moon continually falls toward the earth. Its centrifugal force keeps the moon from actually falling to the earth, and the result is an orbit around the earth. As we have already seen, that orbit is not a pure and fixed one, because of the attractions of the sun and of the earth's equatorial bulge, among others. Every gravitational force must be considered in any problem and not rejected unless it is found to be very tiny.

It is unlikely that Isaac Newton could have arrived at his laws of motion and of gravitation, or even his invention of the calculus, without the previous work of the German, Johann Kepler, who was on the verge of stating all of them when he died in 1630. Using the naked-eye observations of the positions of the planets that were made by his teacher Tycho Brahe, the Dane, Kepler was able to deliver us from the confusion that had reigned throughout the scientific world for so many centuries.

Kepler rejected the philosopher's "perfect" curve, the circle, as the proper path of a planet. Others had tried, by various combinations of circles and epicycles and eccentrics, to explain the motions of the planets. Kepler swept all the mystery away in three statements which we call his laws of planetary motions:

I. The orbit of each planet is an ellipse, with the sun in one focus.

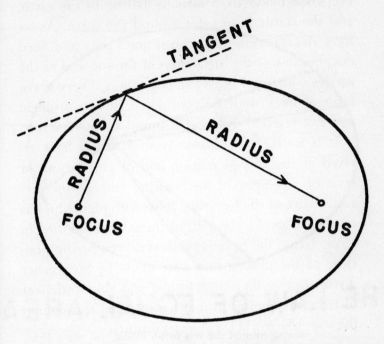

AN ELLIPSE

The orbit of each planet is an ellipse, containing 2 foci (one of which is the sun). The distance from one focus to the circumference and back to the other focus is always a contant. Push two pins into a sheet of paper. Tie a string to the pins and put a pencil in the string and pull it taut. Now, when the pencil is moved around it will trace out an ellipse. As the pins are moved together the ellipse becomes rounder and rounder. Finally, when the pins are together the curve is a circle. When the pins are spread apart the ellipse become flatter and flatter.

II. As the planet revolves around the sun, the line joining it and the sun sweeps over equal areas in equal intervals of time.

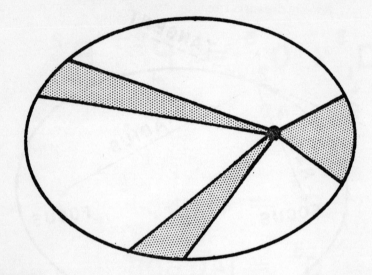

THE LAW OF EQUAL AREA

A planet moving around the sun in an ellipse will move faster when it is closer to the sun and slower when it is farther. Thus, in the case of the earth, when it is closest to the sun in January the earth moves most rapidly. It moves slowest in July. The radius vector—the line joining the earth and the sun—will sweep out equal areas in equal lengths of time. For this reason, when the planet is close to the sun the triangle is short and wide. When it is distant the triangle is long and narrow.

In Chapter 1 we learned that the earth's orbit around the sun is an ellipse and the sun is not at the center but is, instead, more than 1,500,000 miles from the center, at one focus of the ellipse. Therefore

III. The squares of the periods of revolution of two
planets are in the same ratio as the cubes of their
mean distances from the sun.

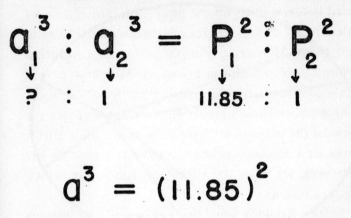

$$a_1{}^3 : a_2{}^3 = P_1{}^2 : P_2{}^2$$

$$? : 1 \qquad 11.85 : 1$$

$$a^3 = (11.85)^2$$

$$a^3 = 140.608$$

$$a = 5.2 \; \textit{Astronomical Units}$$

Jupiter has a period or year of 11.85 years. Using the earth's year
as one and the earth's distance from the sun as one astronomical
unit, we can solve the formula and find that Jupiter is 5.2 times
as far from the sun as is the earth.

the earth is about 3,100,000 miles farther from the
sun at one time of year than it is six months later.
The second law of Kepler tells us that when the earth
is nearest the sun it must travel fastest, because then
its radius vector—the line joining it and the sun—is

shorter. To sweep over the same area in an equivalent interval of time, it must sweep faster.

We might use Pluto and Mercury to illustrate the third law, rounding off the figures somewhat for easy calculation. Pluto's distance from the sun is close to 100 times Mercury's. Pluto's period of revolution around the sun is almost 250 years; Mercury's period is about one-quarter of a year. Pluto's period, then, is about 1000 times that of Mercury. If we square the ratio of the periods, we have 1000 times 1000, which gives us 1,000,000. When we cube the ratio of the distances, we have 100 times 100 times 100, which also is 1,000,000.

Before Kepler's day, the periods of the planets were known but their relative distances from the sun were neither known nor measurable. Kepler's third law, based upon the planets Venus, earth, and Mars alone, made it possible to determine the relative distances of all the planets. When one actual distance, such as that of the earth from the sun, could be determined, all actual distances would then become known.

With the law of gravitation and his calculus, Newton was able to prove that Kepler's laws had to be true. From his work, others were able to go on to methods of calculating at any moment the position of a planet in space, with the sun as a central reference point and the earth's orbit as a fundamental plane. Then the apparent position of any planet as seen from the earth could be calculated. Conversely, if observations of a few positions of a body could be made, we could determine all of the characteristics of its orbit. We call these the elements of the orbit and they are as listed here:

a, the semi-major axis of the orbital ellipse, or the mean distance of the object from the sun; this determines the size of the orbit and the period of revolution.

e, the eccentricity of the ellipse; this determines the shape of the orbit and, with a, the distance from the center to the focus.

i, the inclination of the plane of the ellipse with respect to the earth's orbital plane; this is the "tilt" of the orbit with respect to ours.

☊ the longitude of the ascending node of the orbit, or the point on the ecliptic, the plane of the earth's orbit, where the body crosses the ecliptic from south to north; this determines the direction of the tilt of the orbit.

ω, the argument of latitude, which is the angular distance from the ascending node, measured along the body's orbit plane, to the perihelion point, where it is nearest the sun; this tells the position of the orbital ellipse in its own plane. Sometimes ☊ and ω are added together and called π, the longitude of perihelion.

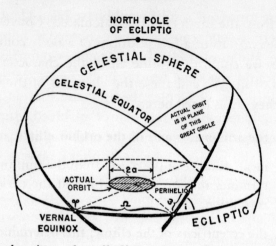

T, the time of perihelion passage, the statement of
the moment when the body is exactly nearest the
sun. From this one statement of the position of
the body in its orbit at a certain time, its place in
its orbit at any other time can be determined.

We must recall that gravitation is a universal
property of all matter. When Newton proved that
Kepler's laws had to be true if the law of gravitation
is true, he was really proving that the same laws
apply to any system of bodies revolving around a
central mass. For example, Jupiter has 12 known
satellites whose motions are exactly in accordance
with Kepler's laws. The fifth one out from Jupiter
is just about 10.4 times as far as the nearest one. Its
period is 33.5 times that of the innermost satellite.
When we cube 10.4 we get 1125; when we square
33.5 we get 1122. If we had used the precise values

of these ratios our results would have been identical.

There is one caution to be observed here, of course. We must stick with the same system, revolving around the same central body, when we apply this third law of Kepler, because the motion of a satellite depends on the masses involved. Jupiter does not pull as strongly on its satellites as the sun does on the planets, because Jupiter's mass is only about one-thousandth as great as that of the sun. So Jupiter's satellites have longer periods than planets would have at the same distances from the sun.

For example, one satellite of Saturn is almost exactly the same distance from that planet as our moon is from earth, yet its period is only one-tenth that of our moon. Saturn's mass is almost 100 times as great as the earth's, so its satellites must travel faster to avoid being pulled in.

What it boils down to essentially is this: the laws of motions of bodies under the influence of gravitation that were devised by mathematicians and astronomers to explain the positions of objects in space can be applied also to the motions of man-made satellites revolving around the earth. By accurate observation of the motions of these new satellites we can learn more about the size and shape of the earth and the strength and distribution of its magnetic and gravitational fields, as well as much that we need to know about the earth's atmosphere and the conditions that exist in outer space, beyond the air.

CHAPTER 3

Escape from the Earth

The problem of getting an object off the earth is only one—but a most fundamental one—of the many and profound difficulties involved in space travel.

We live on the surface of a nearly spherical body whose diameter is almost 8,000 miles. It has mass—6,700,000,000,000,000,000,000 tons of it—and therefore it is endowed with a gravitational field.

This field is limitless, yet if we get far enough away from the earth's surface we can, for all practical purposes, neglect it. How far we must go depends upon the accuracy with which we wish to speak. For example, at a distance of 4,000 miles from the earth's surface the pull is reduced to only one-fourth of that at the earth's surface. At 36,000 miles altitude, the pull is only one-one hundredth of that at the surface. Even at 235,000 miles altitude, we know that the earth's gravitational field is active, because the earth holds the moon in its orbit, but out there the pull is only 0.000283 of that at the surface, yet sufficient to prevent the moon's escape.

In our ordinary experiences we are bound to the earth by this gravitational pull, which we call—for the earth—gravity. Without gravity, we would need foot- and possibly hand-holds to stay here; we might even like to avoid the equatorial regions because there the centrifugal force due to the earth's rotation would tend most strongly to hurl us off into space.

Drop a pencil and it falls to the floor; toss a ball out of a window and it falls to the ground; heave a stone into the air and it turns and is quickly on its way back to the ground. An airplane in level flight is not only working to propel itself forward but is also fighting the force of gravity to stay aloft. Every object is subject to the earth's gravity which pulls it toward the center of the earth. To get away from the earth we must overcome this force by feeding into a vehicle an amount of energy sufficient to free it from this constant hold either entirely, or to a degree sufficient to carry it close enough to another body whose gravitational attraction can then take over.

There are various ways of expressing this energy, but perhaps we can best understand the problem if we imagine what happens to a body which falls to the earth from a great distance.

First, let's imagine an earth without an atmosphere, so there will be no resistance to the fall of the object when it gets close to the surface. Further, let's imagine the earth to be stationary and far removed from any other body, so we can neglect the influence of other gravitational attractions. Now we assume that a particle at a great distance—the astronomer would say at an infinite distance—has simply fallen under the influence of gravity all the way to the earth's surface. The question that interests us here is this: With what velocity does the particle strike the earth?

In high school physics or mathematics this is a common problem, and the answer we derive is a trifle less than seven miles per second. Now, if you throw a ball as high as you can, it travels upward with a certain initial speed, slows down until it no longer rises, then slowly starts to fall, with increasing speed all the way back down until it strikes the earth with the speed that it had as it was hurled upward. In other words, the same speed is necessary to project the ball upward to a certain height as the ball acquires in falling from that height.

If we are on the surface of the earth and wish to shoot something out into space to an infinite distance —to the point where the earth's gravity no longer controls it—we must impart to that object the same speed it acquires in falling to the earth from infinity. This is our seven miles per second. For obvious reasons this figure has been called the velocity of escape.

In theory, the problem of leaving the earth is as simple as that. Acquire an initial speed near the earth's surface equal to seven miles per second and you are on your way through space.

Eventually we shall wish to get away from the earth, and attempts even now are being made to put satellites around the moon (see Chapter 11); but in our preliminary explorations we have sought to establish satellites to circle the earth. To do this, we need to achieve what is known as the circular or orbital velocity—the velocity in an orbit close to the earth's surface. For any planet, this circular velocity is equal to the velocity of escape divided by the square root of the number 2; this root is 1.4142. When we divide our velocity of escape—actually 6.95 miles per second—by 1.4142, we get 4.91 miles per second—the velocity necessary to cause a satellite to orbit near the surface of an atmosphereless earth. While this number may not seem too familiar, when we multiply it by 3600—the number of seconds in an hour—we get a value of 17,684 miles per hour. In accounts of successful satellites this figure, or the round one of about 18,000 miles per hour, is often seen in newspapers and magazines.

Every planet has its own escape velocity, hence circular velocity, determined by two factors. One is the diameter of the planet, the other is the mass or amount of material in it. As we go from planet to planet, we shall find different values of these two factors, hence different values of escape velocity. The larger the planet, if the mass remains constant, the smaller the escape velocity, because we can treat the mass as concentrated at the center of the planet and, on a large planet, we are farther from that center, and the pull is less. If the diameter is the same as the earth's, but the mass is different—say greater—then pull and velocity of escape are greater.

Now that we have established the escape velocity and the circular velocity for the earth, the very cogent question arises: How do we achieve such tremendous speeds? Certainly they are very large as compared with those we encounter in our daily lives. For example, the fastest car has traveled with a speed of over 400 miles per hour. The fastest plane, as of this moment, is the X-2, with an unofficial speed of 2300 miles per hour. The futuristic X-15, unveiled on October 15, 1958, and scheduled to take to the skies in a full-powered flight early in 1959, will probably do about 4,000 miles per hour, which is only a fair start on our 18,000 miles per hour. The important point to remember is that the X-2 and the X-15 are rocket planes, not driven by the more conventional types of engines. Rockets are the only devices that can give us the speeds and travel in the environment that make space travel possible.

Rockets are simple devices, really—like firecrackers, but firecrackers designed to go places rather than simply to explode. When the fuel in a rocket burns, a tremendous volume of gas at high temperature is liberated, and it must go somewhere. By arranging to have the gas discharged through a nozzle, we make the rocket move off in the opposite direction.

The operation of a rocket demonstrates Newton's third law of motion: Action and reaction are equal and are oppositely directed. The exhaust of the gases through the nozzle is the action and the motion of the rocket in the opposite direction is the reaction. Rocket motors are reaction motors.

Reaction is not an unfamiliar principle. The "kick" of a gun is an example; as the projectile is propelled forward by the fast burning of the explosive in the shell, the gun is propelled backward simultaneously. Many have had this experience, while still more have seen reaction working in a toy rubber balloon. When you inflate a balloon and hold its mouth pinched tightly, air under pressure fills the balloon. If you release the mouth of the balloon, the air comes gushing out in one direction and the balloon goes skittering away in the opposite direction. The release of the air is the action; the flight of the balloon is the reaction.

The pressure in the balloon determines the speed with which the air will escape. The volume of air in the balloon determines how long the air continues to gush out. Thus the push or, as the engineer calls it, the thrust is dependent on the amount of air and the pressure. Similarly in a rocket motor the thrust depends on the speed and the mass of gases exhausting through the nozzle.

When the thrust just equals the force of gravity, the rocket will become buoyant and literally float. We are accustomed to see this in films of rocket launchings at the moment of take-off. Continue the thrust, or increase its value, and the push will become great enough to cause the rocket to continue to rise. In most cases the thrust is held constant by burning the fuels at a constant rate, but as the fuels are consumed the rocket gets lighter and lighter; as a result the rocket accelerates, to move faster and faster.

This introduces another important aspect of the rocket problem. Suppose we have a rocket weighing 100 pounds fully loaded. Let us say further that after it has taken off and has reached the point where all the fuel has been consumed, the empty rocket weighs only 25 pounds. If we divide the weight of the fully loaded rocket by the weight of the rocket alone, we obtain what is known as the mass ratio. In our example, the mass ratio is 4. It is obvious that the more fuel can be carried the higher the rocket will go. Thus a high mass ratio is desired by rocket engineers.

The rocket gases emerge from the nozzle with a certain velocity. This is not the limiting velocity of the rocket, but there is an intimate relationship between exhaust velocity, mass ratio, and rocket velocity. Without getting too involved in the mathematical and physical theory, we can say that it works out somewhat like this: Let's suppose that we can achieve a rocket speed of 5,000 feet per second with a mass ratio of 4. If we want to raise our final speed to 10,000 feet per second, then we must have a mass ratio of 16. To double the speed, we must square the mass ratio—multiply it by itself. For a rocket to achieve a final velocity equal to the exhaust velocity, the mass ratio must be 2.72. To achieve a speed twice as great as the exhaust velocity we must have a mass ratio of 7.4, which is the square of 2.72.

These are, of course, theoretical findings. We have said nothing about losses due to gravitational penalties and to resistance of the atmosphere. While these are comparatively small (gravity loss may be 0.45 miles per second, the drag loss 0.15 miles per second, for a typical rocket system), they must be taken into consideration before we can achieve the desired rocket speeds.

To get practical, we know that the fuels we possess today do not permit us to achieve satellite or escape velocity with a single rocket. The mass ratio is too low; the empty weight of the rocket is too great as compared with the rocket plus fuel load weight. So we must find a way to add velocity. One way to do this is to dispose of the empty fuel tanks and any structures not necessary for the further operation of the rocket, after it has been on its way for a while.

Suppose we start with a mass ratio sufficient to get the rocket started on its way. As the rocket ascends and the fuel is consumed, we shall jettison the empty tanks. With the remaining payload another rocket goes into action and the upward motion continues. This is what the engineer calls "staging" rockets. The first successful staging occurred on February 24, 1949, when a Wac-Corporal was mated with a V-2, essentially the original German long-range rocket of World War II. These two were launched as a unit from the White Sands Proving Grounds in New Mexico.

After 60 seconds of firing, the V-2 had carried itself and the Wac-Corporal to an altitude of about 20 miles and was moving at about 2600 miles per hour. At the peak velocity achieved by the V-2, the Wac-Corporal was fired and it continued to rise to an altitude of about 250 miles, reaching a peak speed of almost 5200 miles per hour. The Wac-Corporal could carry a payload of about 50 pounds. If this had been in the form of a small solid fuel rocket in the nose of the Wac-Corporal, this third stage could have achieved a speed of about 10,000 miles per hour and a peak altitude, after coasting, of well over 1000 miles. We can thus see that the way to attain high speeds from rockets moving at nominal speeds is to stage them, to add their individual velocities.

Now let's examine the U. S. Navy Vanguard satellite launcher. This is a three-stage rocket assembly using the advanced Viking as the first stage, firing for about 140 seconds to give a speed of about 3600 miles per hour when the fuel is all consumed at a height of about 35 miles. At this point the second stage, moving with this peak speed, separates from the first stage and begins to fire. In about 120 seconds the fuel is exhausted when the rocket reaches an altitude of 140 miles; the speed is then about 9,000 miles per hour. It continues to coast to an altitude of about 300 miles, at which point the spinning solid-propellant third stage separates and begins to fire. After 30 seconds it has added 9,000 miles per hour of velocity to about 8,500 miles per hour remaining from the first two stages. Thus the satellite velocity of about 17,500 miles per hour is achieved.

This scheme of using the step rocket or staged rocket to reach great speeds is a universal concept, used successfully in the U. S. Army Explorers, the Soviet Sputniks and the U. S. Air Force Pioneer, as well as in Vanguard. There has been considerable publicity disclosing the details of the American staging arrangements, but as yet we know nothing about the precise details of the arrangements for the Sputniks.

Today we must use every advantage we can to obtain sufficiently high speeds to accomplish what we wish. For example, we take advantage of the fact that the earth rotates on its axis once a day. A point on the earth's equator moves eastward with a speed of about 1,000 miles per hour. While not a large fraction of the speed needed to put a satellite in orbit, it is still significant and we take advantage of it by firing our rockets in general in an easterly direction.

The ratio of the sum of fuel and hardware (as we call the rocket itself) to the payload we can put into the sky is something the rocket engineers struggle with constantly. The all-up weight of the Vanguard is 22,000 pounds and the satellite payload is about 21½ pounds. The ratio of fuel and hardware to payload is thus 1,000. For the Explorer, this ratio is about 2,000. While we do not have precise information about the Sputnik-launching systems, we believe that they did not match the "sophistication" of the Vanguard. However, the larger the rocket system, the more rapidly the efficiency improves. In all probability the gargantuan size of the Sputnik launchers brought this ratio down to below 200.

To realize a space station built on a grand scale and thus requiring greater payloads to be hurled into the sky, we need a favorable ratio of fuel and hardware to payload. In the Wernher von Braun and Darrell C. Romick concepts the ratio was assumed as 200 to 1. As we shall see in Chapter 7, these concepts envision the use of three-stage rocket assemblies weighing on the order of 7,000 tons.

However, with the launching of the Atlas satellite on December 19, 1958, there occurred a spectacular break-through in the ratios required. At launching the Atlas weighed about 120 tons, and it put into orbit a satellite weighing almost 4½ tons. Thus the ratio of fuel and hardware to payload dropped precipitously from what was considered an optimum of 200 to 1 to about 25 to 1. While the Atlas did not behave like the conventional satellite launching vehicle, the 150,000 pound boosters were dropped before going into orbit. Thus in essence the Atlas may be considered a two-stage vehicle.

By no stretch of the imagination could the entire 4½ tons of payload be considered usable in the construction of the space station. Much of the rocket material has no use in space. But if we use rocket assemblies like the Atlas for the launching, it is conceivable that the vehicle will be designed to furnish maximum usable material for the erection of the space station. The body and components of the launching vehicle can be used for structures, compartmenting, and details of the final product in space.

The type of fuel used is obviously a very important item in the problem of escape from earth. In the early days of rocketry, the fuel used was solid, a form of gunpowder compressed into a shape that permitted the release of energy at a constant rate. As time went on, engineers became painfully aware that such solid propellants simply did not possess enough energy; moreover, several other drawbacks restricted their use. Once this type of propellant is ignited, it cannot be put out, nor can the firing be speeded up or slowed down. Recently some experiments involving carbon dioxide as a medium for quenching or even slowing down solid-fuel combustion have been made. Sometimes these solid propellants developed tiny cracks or checks invisible to the eye; the flame could find them, however, and the results were not the most desirable.

In America, Dr. Robert H. Goddard began experimenting with liquid fuels after World War I; by the mid-20's he had built a liquid-fueled rocket that worked. From that time onward, research on liquid-fueled rockets accelerated and culminated in the German V-2 with its liquid oxygen and alcohol.

Solid propellants combine the fuel and oxidizer in a single package, either by putting the oxygen directly into the fuel molecule or scattering it through the fuel particles. Whether it be a liquid or solid fuel, oxygen is brought into intimate contact with it; the energy released by this combination is measured in terms of what is called the *specific impulse*. The higher the specific impulse, the more energy per unit is contained in the propellant. Today, solid fuels have specific impulses ranging from 210 to 250 pound seconds per pound. New additives in the future may boost specific impulses up to 300 pound seconds per pound.

Liquid propellants find their primary usefulness in their increased specific impulses. Secondary to this is the increased firing time available; also there is the possibility of throttling the engine—turning it on or off at any instant. Specific impulses for liquid propellants range from 250 to 280 pound seconds per pound today, but tremendous activity in the chemical industry is being directed toward improving these figures. Metals such as boron, beryllium, and lithium are being considered as additives to the fuel, and drastic changes of other kinds also are being suggested. The highest specific impulse we might achieve today in chemical rockets is 375 pound seconds per pound, using liquid hydrogen and liquid fluorine.

CHAPTER 4

Rocket Power of the Future

When we speak of space travel, we are in a realm which we are just now entering and everything beyond this threshold is pure speculation. If anything we say should materialize exactly as we visualize it today, no one will be more surprised than the author. But, because we are projecting into the future, we can't afford the luxury of dogmatism. The future will surely bring with it technological advances we cannot now foresee, as well as more comprehensive understanding of the things of nature. It is probable that new systems of propulsion will be explored of which there is not the slightest inkling today. New knowledge coming out of laboratories devoted to pure science, may eventually bring into focus the shape of things of the future.

Release of large amounts of energy from matter has been a subject for investigation for practically all of man's career on earth. In warfare, explosives have run the gamut from the gunpowder of the Chinese to atomic fission and fusion bombs. We need energy for peaceful purposes, too, and in addition to the sources mentioned in the previous sentence man has used wood, coal, and petroleum fuels, liquid and gaseous. So far, nuclear fission is the top source, but the prospects are good that in time the fusion of hydrogen will also be tapped.

We have seen in Chapter 3 that the engineer pays a tremendous penalty for putting even a small payload in the sky. The early satellites have used 1,000 pounds or more of fuel and hardware to put a single pound into orbit. As rockets and rocket ships become larger and more efficient, this ratio will decrease until it is about 200 to one. A few of the larger nations may succeed in some primitive solutions to the problem, hoping to discover new ideas to improve efficiency. A full scale space travel program with trips to the moon and to the other planets will certainly be undertaken in time, but it will probably be successful only on an international scale, after at least several of the larger nations have agreed to pool their resources and their findings. We can visualize this development as following along somewhat the same lines as that of nuclear energy research and its application for peaceful purposes.

While space travel may be realized through the use of chemical fuels, regular and continued space travel on a grand scale will have to come through a solution to the problem of obtaining the necessary energy in ways other than chemical combustion.

The most obvious thought at this point is one about nuclear processes. Atomic-powered submarines, surface ships, and aircraft are either in use, in building, or in advanced design stages. When we burn a chemical fuel, we combine atoms, altering the electron arrangements outside the nucleus. Pound for pound, the nucleus of the atom can yield a million times as much energy as that obtained from combustion. Our pressing problem is to find some way of releasing this fantastic amount of energy from the atomic nucleus in a usable and controllable form.

The author recalls a long talk he had with one of the most prominent men in the space travel field, in which he suggested that it would be impossible to use nuclear energy because of the enormous temperatures involved and the dangers of vicious radioactive poisoning of the launching area. Temperatures of the order of 10,000 degrees F. pose a problem of what materials can be used, because we know of nothing on earth that can withstand such a temperature. The expert's answer was, "Wait and see." He mentioned that negative prophecy was a most dangerous undertaking. Today, research and engineering developments are accelerating so rapidly that it would seem that the nuclear-powered rocket may be just around the corner.

Let's begin with the fusion of hydrogen nuclei. This process would be one in which some source of great heat would be used to produce the fusion, thus releasing the great energy available as hydrogen atoms combine to produce helium. This energy, in turn, would heat a working material, perhaps as simple as water, which would be vaporized in a high-pressure chamber and would then be exhausted through a conventional rocket nozzle.

Another way of using the energy from either fission or fusion processes will be discussed somewhat later in this chapter. Briefly, we may say here that it involves generation of electricity from the heat of the reactor, and using the electricity to propel atomic fragments through a nozzle. This is the ion motor.

Fusion has not yet been accomplished in a controllable way, although all of us are familiar with the enormous energies released in hydrogen bomb explosions. If we can control it, all that we can do with the fission process, which today we can control, will apply to it as well.

Let's go back to the German V-2 of World War II. This rocket had a specific impulse of 216 pound seconds per pound at sea level and this improves with altitude so that at 25 miles it is 254.* To get a rocket

---

* The specific impulse is the product of the thrust in pounds times the burning time in seconds divided by the total weight of the fuel. In the case of the V-2 this is:

$$\text{Specific Impulse} = \frac{59{,}500 \times 70}{19{,}392} = 216.$$

of this type away from the earth and on its way to launching a satellite requires that 98.4% of the initial load be fuel. This is obviously an impossible device. That is why we must resort to staging, and, currently, at least three stages are required in our satellite program.

If the specific impulse can be raised to about 350 pound seconds per pound, at sea level a satellite can be launched with a two-stage rocket. If the improvement can go to about 600 pound seconds per pound, a single stage will do it. This is obviously a goal to shoot for, because a single-stage rocket would weigh much less per pound of payload; or, with the same weight rocket a much larger payload could be launched.

The specific impulse is directly proportional to the square root of the temperature and inversely proportional to the square root of the molecular weight of the working fluid in the heated stage in the chamber. The specific impulse, then, becomes higher if the temperature is higher, the molecular weight is lower, or both. We are stopped when we try to raise our temperatures without limit, because the materials of the mixing chamber and the nozzle will melt away.

Rocket scientists pick hydrogen as the ideal working fluid. It has a molecular weight of 2. Helium has only twice the molecular weight of hydrogen, but it is a difficult material to handle. Obviously, the material we use must be carried in liquid form, to save space, and liquid helium has a temperature only about 7° F. above absolute zero. It is difficult to procure, to liquefy, and to store.

Molecular nitrogen, quite plentiful, might be used. The molecular weight is 28. After nitrogen, we get into the compounds, such as ammonia, which has a molecular weight higher than that of helium. Hence it should be poor in performance, yet in other ways superior to helium.

As in a conventional chemical-fuel rocket, the nuclear rocket could have a turbo-pump forcing the working fluid into a thrust chamber; in this chamber would be a nuclear reactor to provide the heat and a nozzle through which the gas would be expelled and expanded. There is a propellant section from which the propellant is sent into two areas. Some of it goes directly into the reactor, the rest of it through the motor, to cool it regeneratively. In the reactor there are plates that are delivering up the energy of the nuclear process; as the propellant is passed through the plates it picks up the heat, coming out at a pressure of perhaps 250 pounds per square inch. At the nozzle, it expands to zero pressure, thus providing the necessary thrust.

The nuclear rocket motor then is not so different from a conventional chemical fuel motor. In the latter, the fuel generates its own heat by pure combustion and serves also as the propellant. In the nuclear motor, the fissionable material such as U-235, in a graphite matrix, and equipped with the other reactor elements such as graphite reflectors and cadmium or other control rods, provides the heat that produces the pressure in another material, a fluid such as those we have discussed above. In other words, in this type of motor the propellant has nothing to do with the source of heat; in the chemical rocket, the chemical provides the heat and is also the propellant.

Many rocket engineering groups have worked on such nuclear motors. At the Rocketdyne Division of North American Aviation there is a design that can yield a thrust of 100,000 pounds with a maximum

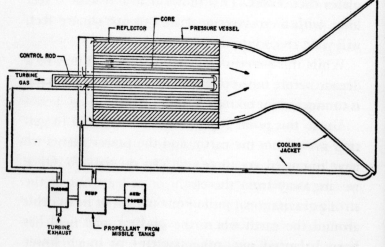

SCHEMATIC OF NUCLEAR ENGINE

Courtesy Rocketdyne

temperature of only 4000° F. The plates in the reactor are an eighth of an inch thick and are separated by the same amount. In the reactor, the hydrogen pressure was chosen as 900 pounds per square inch.

A six-foot-long reactor raises the temperature of the hydrogen to only 3600° F. Engineers compute that they could get a mass velocity of hydrogen passing through the gap at the rate of 40 pounds per second per square foot of gap frontal area. A specific impulse of 790 is also feasible. Dividing the 100,000 pounds of thrust by the 790 gives 127 pounds per second of hydrogen which must flow through the reactor. And if this is divided by 40 (pounds per second per square foot), it gives an area of 3.2 square feet which must be multiplied by two to account for the plates themselves. This shows that a reactor 6 feet long, with a cross-sectional area of 6½ square feet, will yield 100,000 pounds of thrust.

While this concept reads fast and easy, it may be a decade before the application of a device of this type is considered for taking off from earth.

Up to this point we have been interested in getting away from the earth, and the power plants we have discussed are those that can do the job. Once we are away from the earth, or at least out of the strong gravitational pull of our planet, or in an orbit around the earth where the gravitational field has been balanced out, other systems of much lower thrust can be used. In empty space, well away from strong gravitational fields, any thrust, however tiny, will produce an acceleration of the space ship. So some system that could operate over a long period of time with low thrust may serve our purpose.

For example, solar energy is available and perhaps we can harness it. There are several ways in which we could utilize this free energy. For example, a solar power plant here on earth would involve a mirror or other collector of solar energy that would heat a working fluid such as liquid sodium which, in turn, would heat mercury to operate a turbine and generator to produce electricity. We could use this same heat on a working fluid and exhaust it through a nozzle. In the Krafft Ehricke concept of the solar space ship with a two-man crew the ship itself consists of two great shells 128 feet in diameter, made of very thin plastic coated on one side with aluminum to concentrate the radiation of the sun on a working fluid, to heat it up, producing a high pressure. It would then be discharged through a nozzle to expand to zero pressure, thus providing thrust through almost direct solar energy.

Another way of obtaining electricity from sunlight is through the solar battery prepared by the Bell Telephone Laboratories. This application uses the photoelectric-cell principle involving extremely thin silicon wafers "tainted" with a minute quantity of arsenic and boron. The efficiency of this power source, today, is about 11%. If this could be stepped

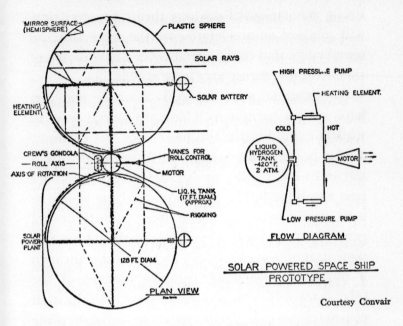

PLAN VIEW

FLOW DIAGRAM

SOLAR POWERED SPACE SHIP
PROTOTYPE

Courtesy Convair

up to about 30%, we could get a voltage high
enough for use in an ion motor, yet to be discussed.

Often in jeweller's or optician's windows there
can be seen a little device called a radiometer. Inside
a glass bulb is a little paddle wheel spinning merrily.
One side of each vane of the wheel is blackened, the
other side is bright. The dark side absorbs energy and
grows warm, the bright side reflects most of the energy away and remains cooler. A molecule in the
bulb will touch the bright side and, receiving little
additional energy, will bounce away with no great
increase in speed. A molecule that collides with the
dark side of a vane receives some heat and picks up

speed. As it bounces away, it gives the vane a kick and makes it move. As we watch the wheel spinning, we are watching the result of the impinging of millions of molecules, each of them imparting an almost negligible kick, all of them adding up to considerable force, at least enough to spin the wheel against the friction of its pivots.

In space, however, it doesn't work out that way because there are such few particles to react with the sails. The radiation pressure from the radiant energy of the sun might be caught by huge, ultra-light weight sails, driving them away much as a sailing ship's sails are driven before the wind. Dr. Richard L. Garwin proposes this mechanism as a drive for space ships.

Radiation pressure is a real, though tiny force. We see it at work, for example, in the fact that tails of comets point away from the sun, the particles of the tail being blown away from the sun as though by a great wind.* Stars are held in equilibrium by radiation pressure from their centers, where energy is generated; this pressure resists and balances the gravitational pull that tries to squeeze the star into a smaller volume.

Dr. Garwin proposes that sails made of a plastic only 1/10,000 inch thick, aluminized on one side, be

---

* While Dr. L. Bierman has demonstrated that corpuscular radiation from the sun is often more effective than radiation pressure in directing the tails of comets, radiation pressure is still significant.

erected on our ships in space; the radiation pressure from the sun would literally push the ship, imparting a tiny but usable acceleration. Such a sail would weigh only about 1/60 ounce per square foot. If we would wish, for example, to increase the velocity of an orbitting Vanguard satellite weighing $21\frac{1}{2}$ pounds, so that it would escape from orbit and go out into space, a sail about 75 yards in diameter would be necessary. The acceleration imparted to the satellite would be about 1/6000 of that due to gravity at the earth's surface.

It would be, in the present or conceivable future state of our knowledge, impossible to use such a feeble force to escape from the earth directly. However, from a satellite orbit it would be possible. The sail could be made collapsible so that as the satellite approaches the sun in one half of its orbit there is no radiation pressure working on it. As the satellite swings past a certain point in its path and begins to move away from the sun, the sail would be unfurled and begin to pick up the pressure that would, little by little, build up velocity to that necessary for escape from the orbit and getting away into space. A small solar battery could be used to furnish the power for this manipulation of the sail. Given time, escape velocity could be achieved. The idea sounds fantastic today, but it may prove to be one of the most economical means of travel in empty space at some future time.

Another system using tiny thrusts over long periods of time has been mentioned earlier. This is the ion rocket which may have a tremendous impact on space travel of the future. Most of the atoms we encounter in the normal course of events on earth are electrically neutral; the positive charge on the nucleus of the atom is exactly balanced by the negative charges of the electrons revolving around the nucleus. A very high temperature or a high voltage discharge tears some of the electrons away, leaving the bulk of the atom with a positive charge. This mutilated atom we call an ion and, having an electrical charge, it can be affected by an electric and a magnetic field and can be accelerated to a high speed. In all probability the electric field will be used for acceleration while the magnetic field will be used for control, focusing, and deflection.

This concept is by no means new, even in its application to rocket propulsion. Many scientists here and abroad have explored its possibilities, and prominent among them has been Dr. Ernest Stuhlinger, who established many fundamental ideas. One interesting concept is Project Snooper, devised by M. I. Willinski and E. C. Orr of North American Aviation.

Project Snooper utilizes a double propulsion system—one to get the rocket away from the earth into space, the other to propel the vehicle after it is in space. The total weight of the Snooper is only 3300 pounds—slightly more than the payload of Sputnik

III—so it could be put into orbit by conventional means, such as a chemical rocket system. Even if nuclear energy were to be used, it might be advisable to use chemical fuels in the first stage to avoid contamination by radioactivity at the launching site. But the nuclear energy should be available for the ion rocket stage, to get from orbit into space.

The intermediate or fast nuclear reactor would use sodium as a coolant to heat mercury to operate a turbine and generator to produce the electricity to create caesium ions. It would also produce the electrical and magnetic field necessary to expel and guide the ions with great speed. The Snooper scheme provides for about 147 kilowatts of electrical energy, much of which would be dissipated in the form of heat. The caesium is stored in liquid state at 100° F., then released through a check valve and sprayed on the walls of a vaporizing cylinder at a temperature of 1400° F. This will create the ions, which are then accelerated by an electrical potential difference of 27,500 volts up to a speed of 125 miles per second. This action is somewhat similar to that used in the atom smashers in our laboratories.

With four amperes of current, these two motors can generate a thrust of one-sixth of a pound each. This thrust will yield an acceleration of one-tenth of a milli-g, in other words, a ten-thousandth of the force of gravity on the earth's surface.

A by-product of each ion is electrons, and these

must be ejected, also, or we shall not have an electrically neutral rocket. The desired electrical fields must be those of our making and control.

The length of the Snooper is about 26 feet, with the wings about 70 feet across. The wings will be coated with a black material to radiate away heat, for it will provide a heat sink for the thermal cycle. The vehicle would go into orbit all wrapped up in a small package which would unfold into its final configuration upon arrival in space.

While the payload can be designed for a variety of tasks, the one of greatest interest is televising or radar-scanning the surfaces of the moon and planets and relaying this information to the earth. Data-transmission systems to make this possible are currently under investigation, and it seems certain that if and when Snooper is operational, these data will reach the earth with high accuracy.

One last method of propulsion will be discussed here. It is really a method for the future—and for the far distant future, at that. With a delicate micro-balance, we can actually measure the energy in a beam of light. If we can produce energy from the total annihilation of matter, on a sufficiently large scale, we can perhaps then proceed to direct the stream of energy in a desired direction, to produce propulsion of a rocket.

In the giant accelerators in the laboratory, and in the natural phenomenon of the cosmic rays, we see total annihilation of matter and the production of the equivalent amount of energy. The mutual annihilation of the electron and positron is well known and fairly easily accomplished. The six billion electron volt bevatron has given evidence of the annihilation of a proton and its negative counterpart, the anti-proton.

Photons of various energy contents result from these reactions and, if the stream could be directed, low accelerations could be produced which, over long periods of time, could build up the speed of a space ship to any desired value.

The rub is, of course, that phrase, "over long periods of time." Inside the solar system, trips involving only a few years might be possible, using these low-acceleration systems for propulsion, once the space ship is away from the earth. Between the stars, the distances are so great that centuries might be involved in the journeys, even if eventually the ship might be going with a speed comparable to that of light itself.

For the foreseeable future, it is likely that nuclear-powered rockets using a working fluid offer the best possibilities. Even with these, however, it is probable that the first stages will be chemically fuelled to avoid radioactive contamination of the launching areas. Perhaps, however, even this difficulty will be overcome by the time the first nuclear rockets are ready to blast off.

CHAPTER 5

Artificial Satellites

In Chapter 3, we saw that to establish a satellite at a moderate distance from the earth we must attain a speed of approximately 18,000 miles per hour. But this is only a part of the story. The satellite will orbit around the earth only if, when it reaches a certain altitude traveling at a certain speed, it is traveling in a certain direction, within rather close limits.

h	V_o
miles	miles per hour
100	17,465
200	17,254
300	17,050
500	16,663
750	16,215
1000	15,801

Suppose we first consider the ideal circular orbit. In the accompanying table, circular velocities V_o are listed according to altitudes h in miles. In order to put a satellite into a circular orbit at one of these altitudes, the object must be moving exactly at the listed velocity at the moment of release and, what is most important, it must be traveling exactly parallel to the earth's surface. The technical term for this last requirement is that the injection angle is zero, for a circular orbit. Perhaps we don't want the satellite to have a circular orbit; there is yet a certain desired angle of injection and it must be held to very close limits if the wished-for orbit is to materialize. Many scientists have studied the problems involved here, to establish the permissible tolerances to establish satellites in orbits.

First we must concede that there is but a remote possibility that a precisely circular orbit will be established. In general the orbit will be an ellipse, with the center of the earth in one focus (see Chapter 2). The point of the ellipse closest to the earth's center, hence the point where the altitude above the earth's surface is least, is called the *perigee;* the opposite point of the ellipse, farthest from the earth's center, is called the *apogee.* If the orbit is a circle, there is, of course, neither perigee nor apogee, and the satellite travels at the same speed throughout its whole path. In the elliptical orbit, the velocity is not constant, although the average will be about the same as in a circle with a mean altitude equal to the average of the apogee and perigee heights of the ellipse.

The elliptical velocity at perigee is greater than the circular orbit velocity; the elliptical velocity at apogee is less than the circular orbit velocity. At both these points and nowhere else in the orbit, the satellite is traveling parallel to the earth's surface.

If, therefore, the satellite enters the orbit with the injection angle equal to zero, but the velocity is too high, the orbit is an ellipse with the injection point as the perigee. The apogee point will be halfway around the earth, at a distance that depends upon how much excess injection velocity is available. The greater the excess over the circular velocity at the injection point, the greater the distance of the apogee from the earth's surface.

If the injection angle is zero, but the injection velocity is less than the circular velocity at that altitude, the injection point becomes the apogee of an elliptical orbit, and the perigee, on the opposite side of the earth, will be closer to the surface of the earth by an amount depending upon the deficiency in injection velocity as compared with that required for a circular orbit.

Recall, now, that the preceding two paragraphs have assumed that the injection angle is zero; that is, at the moment of injection, when the last stage of the rocket ceases firing, the satellite is traveling parallel to the earth's surface. Now, let's see what happens if the injection angle is not zero—if the third stage of the rocket is nosing upward or downward (because of the failure of some control) when it ceases to fire.

Let's suppose first that we have the proper velocity for a circular orbit, the satellite is injected at the proper altitude, but the injection angle is not zero. There again will be an elliptical orbit, of a size and shape depending on the error and direction of the injection angle. But in this ellipse the injection point is neither the perigee nor the apogee, although of course it is a point on the orbit.

What are the limits of velocity and injection angle errors within which the satellite must be launched to move practically in a predetermined orbit? A very comprehensive study of these factors has been made by many people in many fields. Jorgen Jensen of the Martin Company has come up with some very interesting results. Let's examine some of his findings.

The reference altitude for the point of injection has been chosen as 300 miles, and all discussion pertains to this altitude. If the injection velocity is 50 feet per second less than the 24,976 feet per second required for a circular orbit at that altitude—again assuming the injection angle to be zero—the perigee altitude will drop to 270 miles, while the apogee altitude will remain at 300 miles. If the velocity is too high at the injection point, by this same 50 feet per second, the apogee will rise to 330 miles, while the perigee will remain at 300. The curve of change of perigee and apogee altitudes that can be drawn tells us that there is a change of 60 miles for every 100 feet per second excess or deficiency in the injection velocity.

An error in the injection angle also affects the

perigee and apogee altitudes, as we have seen. For an
injection point of 300 miles, we assume the correct
circular velocity. An error of 1½ degrees in the injection angle, with the final stage of the rocket still
climbing (as will usually be the case), results in an
elliptical orbit with perigee altitude of 200 miles
and apogee altitude of 400 miles. The changes in
perigee and apogee altitudes are now equal, but in
opposite directions, and amount to about 65 miles
per degree error in the injection angle. Error in injection velocity produces a change in only one altitude, either perigee or apogee, but not in the other.

It should be apparent that injection point errors
will affect also the period of the satellite—the time
required for one revolution around the earth. By
Kepler's third law of motion (see Chapter 2), the
larger the orbit the longer the period. If the injection velocity is too great, the orbit becomes larger,
hence the period is longer; if the injection velocity
is too small, the orbit is smaller and the period is
shorter. For each 100 feet per second error in injection velocity the period of the satellite changes by
almost 70 seconds in a 300-mile-high orbit, whose
circular period should be 94.3 minutes. This is a
change, then, of about 1¼% for an error of less than
half of 1% in the velocity.

It should be clear that it is almost impossible to
achieve, at least in these early days of satellite technology, exactly the proper velocity and the zero (or

any other desired) injection angle, at a certain altitude. We shall always be subject to both velocity and injection angle errors, but a reasonable criterion has been established for the 300-mile orbit. If we can inject satellites into orbit with an injection angle error of no more than 2¼ degrees and no more than 1% (about 250 feet per second) error either way in the injection velocity, we shall feel that we have done very well indeed.

Suppose we cannot inject the satellite into orbit exactly at 300 miles, although the injection angle and velocity are correct for that altitude. An error of one mile in injection altitude brings a change of about 2.3 seconds in the period of the satellite.

As we shall learn in Chapter 7, we shall wish to establish space stations, some of them manned, at various distances from the earth. These will serve as weather reconnaissance stations, as launching platforms for interplanetary travel, as well as for other purposes. One of these, about 1075 miles high, would orbit the earth each two hours; another, at an altitude of about 22,600 miles, would revolve in 24 hours, as the earth does; so it would remain stationary over a certain point of the earth, if launched in an equatorial orbit in the direction of the earth's rotation.

The construction of a space station requires that we send up a string of satellites to rendezvous in the same orbit. From what we have seen of the effects of injection errors, we can certainly conclude that we must improve our technology before we can hope to make such rendezvous. By the time we have successfully assembled a complex of space stations, we shall have learned enough to make it relatively easy every time.

Obviously, the Sputniks, Explorers, and Vanguards have fulfilled the criteria for orbits of some kind. Some of them have had excess injection velocities and have gone into long orbits. The "baby" Vanguard I is an example, with perigee at 405 miles, apogee at 2465 miles. The Sputniks I, II, and III must have had too-low injection altitudes or depressed injection angles, because their perigee points have been low—less than 150 miles high. While we cannot as yet achieve perfect control to attain the exact criteria to establish a predetermined orbit, we know we can put satellites into the sky. We know of no satellite launcher in which all stages have fired that has not put a satellite into orbit. This fact is a tribute to the guidance systems incorporated in these devices. Apparently we are on the right track.

All satellites established thus far have been more or less instrumented, to provide information about the upper atmosphere or radiations from space, or both. Their weights have determined how much instrumentation can be carried and how much knowledge can be gleaned from their careers. And, of course, these weights have been determined pretty closely by the propulsion systems available to put them into orbit.

Vanguard I weighs only 3¼ pounds and is a sphere a trifle less than 6½ inches in diameter. The only information it sends to the earth is the temperature of the satellite itself. The tiny radio transmitter in this satellite is powered by solar batteries—photo-electric devices that transform solar energy into electricity—and, inasmuch as Vanguard I is believed to have a lifetime of the order of 200 years, we should be receiving this temperature information for a long time to come. The radio transmitter is temperature sensitive; there is a change of frequency of its transmitted radio waves with a change of temperature. Thus, the point on the receiver dial where this signal comes in is an index to the temperature of the satellite. The Vanguard I is the smallest instrumented satellite launched.

The U. S. Army satellites Explorers I and III have weighed about 31 pounds; Explorer IV weighs about 38 pounds. The payloads have been half of these gross weights, or more, and a variety of intelligence has been forthcoming. Cosmic ray intensity, temperatures outside and inside the satellites, and the frequency of impacts from micrometeorites—tiny bits of cosmic debris—are some of the bits of information we get from them. These facts are not wasted if no one is listening in, in at least one of the Explorers. A tape recorder leisurely collects the information throughout its whole orbit, then obligingly rattles it all off, in a terrific hurry, when an interrogating signal from the ground tells it to do so. The transmitter and tape playback operate only when asked to do so.

The most fully-instrumented satellites have been the Soviet Sputniks. A brute-strength rocket assembly was used to hoist tremendous payloads into the sky, and a correspondingly greater variety of experiments could be initiated. Sputnik II weighed 1120 pounds and contained considerable instrumentation of the type included in American satellites, to measure radiations in space. But there was also a biological specimen, a dog whose physical reactions were transmitted back to earth by an intricate system of instruments. Space scientists thus learned for the first time something about the effects of high accelerations and the behavior of an animal under sub-gravity conditions over an extended period.

While there has been considerable talk concerning the dog Laika in gravity-free space, this is a misconception, because Sputnik II was tumbling with a four-second period. Unless the center of rotation passed through the dog's ears, where the vestibular organs are located, there was a small centrifugal force that simulated a low-gravity but not a gravity-free condition. It is difficult to arrive at the magnitude of the centrifugal force because we do not know the location of the dog with respect to the axis of the four-second rotation. But if the dog's head was five feet from the center of rotation, the centrifugal force amounted to about 11 feet per second—about a third of the value of the gravitational acceleration at the earth's surface.

The most elaborate space physical laboratory went aloft in Sputnik III, which weighed 2925 pounds, of which 2130 pounds comprised the instruments and the necessary power supply. Here again were solar batteries to augment the power available from the more conventional chemical-type batteries. Information released by the Soviet I.G.Y. Committee indicated that there were three groups of instruments in Sputnik III. The first was a battery of instruments to check solar radiations, cosmic rays and the density of micrometeorites in space. The second group was concerned more with the earth, probing such conditions in the earth's atmosphere as pressure, composition, degree of ionization, as well as the strength and variation of the earth's magnetic field at high altitudes. The Soviet report pointed out that for the first time it was possible to have the same instruments checking so many features of the earth and its atmosphere at so many levels in the same laboratory.

The third group of instruments in Sputnik III served the others, concerning itself with maintaining regulation over them and relaying the information to the earth. Included were the radio transmitters, temperature regulators, and the program control systems that activated the various instruments at the proper times. Truly this is a formidable complement of instruments—the first considered reasonably complete.

With time, the satellites already launched will tell us where we must extend our studies, where we can be less intense, and where we must plug up gaps now existing. Certainly greater payloads will be lofted as time goes on, so we shan't need to be so skimpy and resort to such extreme miniaturization as has characterized some of the American satellites. We shall be able to develop satellites that will be veritable eyes for the scientists, to reveal vast quantities of significant information about the earth itself and its region in space.

Not all satellites need to be instrumented to be of value. The author in 1954 presented a paper before the Fifth International Astronautical Federation Congress in which he showed that an inert object simply reflecting sunlight could furnish significant geodetic and other information.* The earth's oblateness can be more precisely determined from a careful study of the motions of such a satellite, as can be also the average value of gravity for the entire earth, away from the local anomalies that sometimes disturb readings taken at the surface.

* On October 22, 1958, at 11:21 p.m. a United States Army Jupiter-C missile was fired from Cape Canaveral to establish a "beacon." This was a collapsed 12-foot plastic balloon covered with aluminum foil to be inflated with nitrogen gas when in orbit. The attempt was unsuccessful and the missile fell into the South Atlantic.

As a point-of-light beacon, it can be used for exact triangulation to determine distances between land areas separated by large bodies of water. The moon is used for this purpose today, but it not only is not a precise point in the sky but it also has a somewhat troublesome motion because of the disturbance of the sun. From measurements of the moon, some of our terrestrial measurements are off by 1000 feet or more. With a satellite beacon, it is conceivable that these same distances can be determined to within 100 feet.

The satellite that will attract most attention will be that one which contains a human passenger. The manned satellite will mark the beginning of a new phase of space exploration, because it will be necessary to get the passenger back safely to earth.

As we have seen in Chapter 3, the X-15 rocket plane is designed to achieve a speed in excess of 4,000 miles per hour and an altitude above 200 miles. The altitude is not too important, because as far as a human being under space conditions is concerned the difference between 20 and 200 miles is not too great. What is important is that the speed will be double that attainable for manned flight at the present writing.

This increased speed will give the pilot a chance to check procedures for a return from a manned satellite. He will be coming in essentially without power, and he will be using the aerodynamic forces on his plane to support him as he descends. Success in this venture may open up new means of destroying satellite velocity to effect a return to earth. Heavy equipment such as tanks has been dropped from the sky by parachute, and high-speed military planes today are braked by parachutes that open on the ground as the planes taxi in. To land the X-15 plane by parachute may be feasible, but the size of the payload and the size and weight of the parachute necessary may be prohibitive. Later, new planes will be built, to fly higher and faster than the X-15, and again the big challenge will be to land them safely. When this has been met, man will try returning from flight in a ballistic missile, as already mice, monkeys, and dogs have done; and then at last he will go into space in an orbiting satellite from which he will return safely to earth.

The lifetime of a satellite depends on the density of the object and the altitude of the perigee. If the satellite is dense—that is, heavy for its size, as was Sputnik I—then the resistance of the atmosphere will retard it less than if it were large and had the same weight. The larger the satellite, the more area the atmosphere has to act on, to produce braking action. And, of course, the lower the satellite dips into the atmosphere, the denser the air and the greater the resistance to the motion of the object. Sputnik I was launched October 4, 1957, and fell to earth on January 4, 1958. The last rocket stage that carried the satellite to orbit fell in even less than three months, because of its less favorable mass-area ratio. The satellite itself was spherical, 23 inches in diameter and weighing 184 pounds. The spherical shape is a very favorable one, giving the object the smallest area for its volume and weight, but the perigee point was only about 140 miles above the earth's surface, where the atmosphere still has considerable resistance. This was the determining factor in the short lifetime.

Explorers I and III were the same in dimensions and weight—tubular, 80 inches long, 6 inches in diameter, 31 pounds—but the perigee of the first one was at an altitude of 225 miles while that for Explorer III was only 125 miles. Launched on March 26, 1958, Explorer III fell on June 27, after only three months. Explorer I, launched January 31, 1958, is predicted to have a lifetime of from three to five years. In other words, the almost double perigee altitude of Explorer I made a difference in lifetimes by a factor of about 12 times.

The baby Vanguard I was launched on March 17, 1958, and should stay up for at least 200 years, because its perigee was at an altitude of 405 miles, well above most of the frictional effects of the atmosphere.

Sputnik II, cone-shaped, 15 feet long, weighing 1120 pounds, was launched on November 3, 1957, and fell on April 14, 1958. Both its unfavorable shape and its unfavorable mass-area ratio contributed to its early fall; also, its perigee altitude was only 140 miles.

Working in its favor were the total size of its orbit—apogee altitude was 1025 miles—and the higher orbital velocity at perigee.

The action of the atmosphere on a satellite is to retard the object at perigee, stealing some of its kinetic energy—its energy of motion. This causes the apogee point to move in toward the earth by much more than the change in perigee. We might say that a small change in perigee velocity prevents the object from whipping so far out on its next journey to apogee. The net result is to circularize the orbit, making it less elliptical as the apogee altitude approaches the perigee altitude in value, until the retarding action tends to be equal throughout the whole orbit. Then the satellite descends sharply to burn out by friction with the air or to break up on its way to the earth's surface.

At the moment of writing, we are certain that parts of the satellites or last-stage rockets have not dropped solid portions of their structures on the earth. However, if by any chance a satellite should survive, a question of great significance is at once raised: Who owns it?

This is a question that may be thrust on an unprepared world at any moment now, and it is destined to become more cogent in the near future. Some precept of international law must be brought to bear on this question and realistic answers must be forthcoming.

The urgency of these questions was pointed up at the Ninth International Astronautical Federation Congress meetings in Europe in late summer of 1958. A session in The Hague concerned itself primarily with this problem directly under the statement: "The responsibility of the States for the damage caused by the launched space bodies." Legal minds insisted on the regulation of liability based on an accepted principle of air law, that third persons, having no relation with air traffic, must be protected as much as possible.

Dr. I. H. Ph. de Rode-Verschoor delivered a paper dealing with this subject. She feels that because of the cost of launching satellites only nations can engage in this enterprise and new regulations are necessary for State-owned spacecraft. She assumes that the States must be completely responsible for the behavior of the satellites they launch. The basis for this responsibility lies in the principle that "the States have the duty to avoid damage, because by creating a source of danger one incurs responsibility to the community."

Dr. de Rode-Verschoor gives three solutions to the question of liability:

1. The State that launches the spacecraft can accept full responsibility for possible damage (in accordance with the Convention of Rome, where one knows the principle of risk).

2. The State can be entitled to make certain reservations, as for example in accordance with the Convention of Warsaw (principle of liability of fault), excluding, for instance, responsibility in case of *force majeure* (an example might be the unforeseen collision of the satellite with a meteorite).

3. There could be established an International Guaranty Fund for paying for the damage caused by falling satellites (except in case where the damage is intentional, in which event the State responsible will have to pay for the damage). Each State interested in astronautics and its development would deposit a sum of money in the fund.

She believes that the optimum solution would be the third one, in view of the risks and uncertainties of satellites. If such a Fund should come into being, it could be administered by the United Nations; most experts believe that eventually all control of traffic in outer space should reside with the United Nations.

Serious thinking in the field of this problem is overdue. One of these days a satellite will make a spectacular descent and there will be damage or injury. Before that time arrives, let us hope that the United Nations will have set in motion the processes to meet this contingency.

CHAPTER 6

Uses of Satellites

It is almost impossible to over-emphasize the economic benefit which will accrue to the first nation that manages to establish a manned space station. Disregarding the possible military and psychological advantages, the plain dollars-and-cents value will be incalculable in the purely peaceful matters of weather forecasting, communications, accurate mapping, and basic scientific research.

In the past few years, ingenious and gifted scientists from many countries have studied the uses of satellites, and the more they investigate the uses the more they appreciate how tremendous a boost to knowledge will come from these manmade moons. Perhaps the field which interests the layman more than any other is that of forecasting weather.

In most cases it is difficult to convince the layman that the satellite will enhance his well-being and make a better life for him. The results of investigations of the atmosphere, of radiations, leave him cold. He is in the position of saying: What is in it for me? The answer to this can be given only in terms of weather. This feature of the future satellite program the layman can understand and appreciate.

At this time there is a tendency to disparage the weatherman. When he makes an inaccurate forecast he is classed as an incompetent, in spite of the fact that he is right approximately 80% of the time. What is not generally realized is that the weatherman receives reports about conditions from only about 4% or 5% of the surface of the earth. The remainder is not covered by weather stations. Yet from this tiny hold we expect forecasts with 100% accuracy. It simply cannot be done, at least at this time. However, when a space station is set up for recording weather patterns, forecasts may achieve well-nigh perfect reliability.

There was a time when meteorologists seemed aloof concerning applications of space stations to weather problems, but today many experts in the field look forward to the advent of global forecasting. They realize that they are badly handicapped in their present forecasts because at best they must rely upon observations by instruments carried to puny heights by planes and balloons. They realize that any forecasting, by human reasoning or by electronic calculations, could be highly improved if data were obtainable from far above the earth.

One expert, Dr. Harry Wexler, chief of the scientific services division of the United States Weather Bureau, has described what type of space station will be most valuable in weather forecasting. He believes that to reconnoiter weather conditions most effectively the station should possess the following characteristics:

It should be at least 4,000 miles above the surface of the earth, where it would have a period of revolution of 4 hours. It would circle the earth six times during the 24-hour day, permitting the weather observer to be over a particular part of the earth twice, that is, once in each direction of motion, each 12 hours. The westward component of the motion of the station due to the spinning of the earth means that new storms could be detected. At the suggested height the weather satellite would permit the observer to have an instantaneous view comparable to the area of North America and the adjacent oceans, about equal to the working area the forecaster uses today.

Dr. Wexler speculates on the nature of reflections from the earth and the clouds, and concludes that the overall result would be to give a bluish tinge to what is seen. This appears contrary to popular notions, but the scattered blue light from the incident

solar beam would more than make up for the lack
of blue reflected from the ground. As the observer
looked off toward the horizon, he would see a gray
layer with an upper blue layer and a black region
above that.

In a hypothetical weather picture over Amarillo,
Texas, at 4000 miles, the following might be found:
Three storms may be present, in various stages of
development, extending from Hudson Bay to Texas.
A fully developed hurricane is found in the West
Indies. There is a line-squall—the favorite breeding
ground of severe wind storms and tornadoes—in the
east, moving ahead of a cold front. There are scattered cumulus clouds of various thicknesses over
heated land areas. Finally, there are fog and low
stratus clouds over the California coast, the Great
Lakes, and the Newfoundland area, formed by the
passage of warm air over the cold surfaces.

From such a station, the meteorologist could be
given a clear picture of the cloud distribution and
could with little difficulty sketch in a useful chart
showing the locations of the various stormy and fair
weather areas. Obviously, this "bird's-eye view"
would yield a better idea of the large-scale weather
distribution than an earthbound weatherman can obtain from scattered observations taken at or near the
earth's surface.

The passage of the station over storm areas twice
during each 12 hours would permit the close tracking

of storms and the observation of storm origin and development. In some instances, the same clouds that make possible the visual identification of the storm will hide its location with respect to the surface features. The accuracy of tracking these large storms from the station alone will sometimes not be too good, but fortunately they move slowly. The faster-moving incipient or embryonic storms have a less extensive cloud system associated with them, so that more accurate fixes could be obtained. A hurricane with its open "eye" at the center, and cloud systems associated with cold fronts and squall-lines will lend themselves to easier tracking.

A manned station would be the ideal setup but, if this proves too difficult, a television satellite storing the information on videotape and transmitting it to the earth on demand could furnish the picture.

Actually a manned space station opens up a great many other possibilities. At the station the temperature of the earth's surface, and a rough average temperature of the intervening atmosphere could be obtained. Precipitation areas could be detected by radar and their heights above the earth's surface measured. Thunderstorms could be located by the accompanying lightning either visually at night or electronically by day. Solar radiation measurements, particularly in the ultraviolet, would serve to correlate weather and solar outbursts. The reflectivity of the earth's surface could be determined for various land and water areas, and finally the sampling of meteoritic dust could be made to test the theory that these particles serve as cloud-seeding agents for rain.

Even before the establishment of the ideal weather station in space, significant weather information can be obtained. Certainly if pictures could be recovered from temporary satellites they could disclose storms. On October 5, 1954, an Aerobee rocket was launched from the White Sands Proving Grounds; the resulting photographs disclosed two patterns of spiral cloud bands with the possibility of a third. These are characteristic signatures of hurricanes, although the surface weather maps showed no signs of these tropical storms. Here is a very graphic illustration of what may happen because at the surface we cannot make sufficiently complete observations for proper weather forecasting.

One kind of special satellite today could yield fundamental meteorological information—the energy balance of the earth. Small spheres, about the size of ping-pong balls, could be mounted on the four tips of the radio antenna of the satellite, with three of the balls possessing different radiation-absorbing characteristics.

One of the spheres would be white to visible radiation but black to long-wave or infrared radiation. The second would be black to visible radiation and gray to infrared. The third would be black to both visible and infrared radiation. If the temperatures of the three spheres were measured each 30 seconds, or for a 150-mile track, the information derived would be susceptible to mathematical analysis to derive the incoming solar radiation, the reflected solar radiation, and finally the infrared radiation sent into space by the earth and its atmosphere. A satellite moving in a belt from 40 degrees north latitude to 40 degrees south could yield the net gain of radiation in this belt of the earth, and a daily account of this energy difference would reveal time variations. These could then be correlated with atmospheric flow disturbances to provide a clue to major changes in this important weather factor.

The distribution of albedo, or reflecting power, of the earth and atmosphere could also be determined, from the ratio of the reflected solar radiation to the incoming radiation, as the satellite traverses its orbit. This would reveal reflection variations caused by differences between land, ocean, snow, and—most important—cloud areas. It should be possible to identify the presence of large cloud areas, particularly over the oceans where the background brightness would be generally low. It should be possible to differentiate between the bright, high-reaching clouds associated with active storm areas or the duller clouds of incipient hurricanes.

Thus, from satellites to be launched in the immediate future or from more sophisticated satellites of a more distant future, there is certainly one benefit to be derived; and that is the better knowledge of the weather that plays such an important role in our lives.

But the weather is only one project of many that can be tackled with satellites. On July 1, 1957, a scientific effort on a global scale officially began, to extend to December 31, 1958. It is called the International Geophysical Year (I.G.Y.). The efforts of scientists all over the world were to be combined for a massive assault on the scientific frontiers. Many of the efforts were to be purely geophysical in nature, following more or less conventional lines, but a considerable number were tied to the ability of man to put satellites into the sky and to probe the secrets of nature from high above the surface of the earth. As we all know now, these satellites were successfully launched, and fantastically productive results have come from them.

Outer space will be the finest experimental laboratory man can have. There the scientist will find a variety of conditions which cannot be duplicated on earth, yet are necessary to the pursuit of the aims of science.

There is an absence of gravity in a space station. While it is true that gravity can be simulated by a rotation of the space station (see the following chapter), it is possible to provide an area where gravity does not exist—where the gravitational pull of the earth is exactly balanced by the centrifugal force of the motion of the satellite in its orbit. Biological experiments can be pursued free of gravitational forces. The growth and behavior of animal and plant life under gravity-free conditions presents an unprecedented challenge to the zoologist and botanist. Will plants in a weightless environment grow taller, will they be bulkier, or will a spreading action take place due to the lack of weight? Obviously, plant life on the earth is working every minute of the day against the force of gravity. Remove this force and, in a manner of speaking, the plant ceases working. Interesting conjectures can be made about the future behavior of plant life in space.

The human being is also working against gravity. What is the long-range physiological trend to be expected in this case? Some writers have suggested that gravity-free regions such as a space station, or low-gravity regions such as the moon, where the pull is but a sixth of that on earth, would be ideal places for convalescents. These, especially if they had a cardiac condition, would not have to work against the force of gravity; even the blood would not have to flow against a gravity "head." People in traction would not have to worry about remaining immobile, because the member in question would possess no weight and thus would not move to the discomfort of the patient.

A wide range of temperatures is found in space, although in a space station it may be easily possible to hold the temperature at a comfortable level. On that side of the station away from the sun the temperature will go down to perhaps 100° F. below zero. On the side of the space station toward the sun, concentrators of solar radiation can raise the temperature to that of the surface of the sun itself—11,000° F. The significant point here is that these temperatures, both low and high, can be applied under conditions of zero gravity. Experiments involving temperatures can be performed in space which under no circumstances could be performed on earth. With no gravity, liquids would have only surface tension acting on them and would ball up and always assume a spherical shape. These liquids could be subjected to high temperatures without our worrying about containers for them. Metallurgical experiments could be performed under unique conditions; no crucibles are needed. When the metal is put into the desired area, it stays there.

Experiments dealing with electronics—in which hard vacua are essential—would be easily performed on the space station. The behavior of electronic components under these conditions can guide the engineer on earth in his future applications of electronic systems. The problem of operating transistors or electronic tubes is a crucial one. Not only vacuum, but also temperatures constitute major problems. If there are batteries, the temperature must not drop below 20° F. or go above 140° F., otherwise their efficiencies drop precipitously. Thus the establishment of a space station will provide the answers which will guide the planners of space flights of the future.

Both physical and chemical experiments could be performed under conditions of combinations of gravity-free space, a wide range of temperatures, and intensities of radiations in space.

Contrary to popular belief, the sun is not a quiet body; it undergoes sporadic disturbances which in turn affect the earth. A hydrogen flare on the sun emits vast amounts of ultraviolet radiation. And the sun-spots where the flares normally occur act as giant howitzers in that they bombard the earth with electrons and the hearts of hydrogen atoms, protons. These particles traverse the 93,000,000 miles separating the earth and the sun in from 26 to 40 hours, and give rise to the only visible terrestrial manifestation of the solar storms—the aurora borealis and aurora australis, the northern and southern lights. These can be seen as sheets, rays, and curtains of eerie light, sometimes covering almost the whole sky.

There are other more subtle effects of solar storms. Most of our normal communication devices are tied to the concept of a stable magnetic field for the earth. In them are built delicate relays that function very well as long as the magnetic field behaves itself. But when a solar storm occurs, one of the effects is a warping and disturbance of the earth's magnetic field. The consequence is that the little electromagnetic components so dependent on a stable magnetic field no longer function properly; long distance telephone, telegraph and teletype machines begin misbehaving and, instead of an intelligible message, a lot of gibberish is seen and heard.

Even the power companies are at the mercy of these solar storms, 93,000,000 miles away. The influx of particles from the sun gives rise to tremendous ground currents of thousands of amperes which in some instances burn out circuit breakers at the power distribution centers with subsequent power failures all along the line.

The space station will be able to monitor the particles before they get to the earth and perhaps a warning system can be set up to eliminate the possibility of failures in our services. Another possibility that would be desirable would be advance notice to people that a display of the aurora is imminent. Thus many could get out away from city lights and perhaps for the first time in their lives see this strange and impressive phenomenon.

Our atmosphere shields us from most of the radiations from space, but a space station will permit us to sample these radiations to fill out our picture of what is really present there. Man on the surface of the earth little realizes how intimate is the relation between these incoming radiations and his present-day life. As an example, we listen to a foreign broadcast, or perhaps we speak by trans-Atlantic telephone. Radio waves are used to propagate these signals. As we have seen in Chapter 1, there are layers of electrons high above the earth's surface, and shattered atoms—ions—which act as mirrors to reflect radio waves back to the surface, around the horizon's bulge. Take away these reflecting layers and long-range radio communications cease. And, by the same token, if there is a disturbance on the surface of the sun, such as a hydrogen flare at the eruption of a sun-spot group, the influx of more and more energetic particles and radiations will create havoc high up in our atmosphere, making the reflecting layers bob up and down and increasing the total number of ions, to absorb the energy in radio signals, producing unwelcome fading.

Putting the proper satellites in the sky may furnish the means for establishing a fool-proof system of long-distance communications. Radio engineers today have devised schemes in which they can reflect radio waves from objects to identify them; the familiar radar is an example of this. They have also found that they can build what they term transponders. These are devices that receive a signal and immediately amplify and retransmit it. Thus, if we had a space station acting as a transponder, engineers on the earth could use it to reflect signals back to the earth to points far away from the original transmitter. A single one would not be sufficient. Many of them should be put into the sky so that a transponder might always be available for rebroadcast purposes.

The noted writer Arthur C. Clarke has suggested that if the satellites could be established some 22,600 miles above the surface of the earth in 24-hour orbits, each could be arranged to be stationary over some point of the earth. A signal sent to one of these transponder satellites would be transmitted to the other two and to all points of the earth beneath, literally blanketing it with radio or television signals. The political aspects of a system like this as a propaganda weapon are staggering. The only hope of the world is that by the time this system can materialize the political picture will become much brighter and more stable than it is at present.

With accurate time available to observation stations, a satellite can be used in a variety of ways for geodetic purposes. In Chapter 5, the author has already indicated that uninstrumented satellites, merely reflecting sunlight, can serve this purpose. Using such a beacon revolving around the earth, observers can make possible the measurement to high accuracy of distances across large bodies of water—accuracy of the same order as that prevailing in the triangulation of areas of the earth's land surface.

We know the distance between Washington, D.C., and the West Coast with an uncertainty of perhaps 25 feet. We know the distance from Washington to

Paris with an uncertainty of about 1000 feet. The reason for this uncertainty is that we must use the moon for one of our triangulation points, and the astronomer is slightly embarrassed in not knowing precisely how the moon moves. Were we to put a beacon satellite in the sky and observe it accurately from many stations with a coördinated time system of high accuracy, we could reduce the uncertainty in the Washington to Paris distance to below 100 feet.

Another factor important to the astronomer and the geophysicist is the average value of gravity for the whole earth. The behavior of the beacon would be an index to this value and thus would provide a means for detecting anomalies in the structure of the earth's outer shell. Finally, our earth is not a perfect sphere, but is flattened at the poles. The classic value of the oblateness is one part in 297. Because the beacon could be photographed against the background of the stars and its position determined to a high degree of accuracy, the measure of the exact shape of the earth could be accomplished, also to a high degree of accuracy.

One last use of satellites that will be mentioned here is the thorough investigation of the meteoroid content of space. These space bullets are of various sizes, from microscopic grains to objects that can be considered small planets. Many of them are large enough to destroy even a large satellite or space ship. If man is to venture out into the space between the planets, it is essential that he have some idea of the magnitude of the hazard. A satellite circling the earth beyond the protective atmosphere will be able to record the impact of meteoroids from the tiniest which may not even mar the paint on the satellite to the larger ones which may cause significant damage. Many astronomers and statisticians have combined efforts of observation and calculation to determine the sizes and the numbers of these objects, but this very necessary census can be correctly made only by means of a satellite revolving around the earth at very high altitude.

CHAPTER 7

The Space Station

There is a space station in the sky that you can see for perhaps 20 days a month. It is plainly visible; we call it the moon. Our moon circles the earth locked to it by the gravitational attraction of the earth. It is endowed with a motion which prevents it from being drawn down into the earth, and this same motion makes the moon fall around the earth in the period of a month.

In the case of the moon we see the neat balance of forces necessary to establish a satellite of the earth—for indeed the moon is the natural satellite of the earth. A long time ago—perhaps five or six billion years—the earth-moon system came into being. Just how this came about we don't know; perhaps we may find out when man gets to the moon, or perhaps we may never know the origin of the moon. But when the moon was born it was endowed with the precise amount of centrifugal force to balance the gravitational pull of the earth and, as a result, the moon falls around the earth. Every time the moon moves a half-mile in its orbit, it falls one-twentieth of an inch toward the earth. If these steps are smoothed out, what we get is the path of the moon around the earth.

The moon will continue circling the earth for a long time—on the order of tens of billions of years. The reader may ask: Doesn't this violate what we have been taught in school? We were always taught that there is no such thing as "perpetual motion." If we want to make something move, we must furnish energy for it. Once the energy stops, the object stops moving. While this is true for objects on the earth, it does not work out that way for the moon. At that long-ago time, the moon was endowed with sufficient energy to set it swinging around the earth. There is no friction, so the moon keeps on going.

The reason for this discussion of the motion of the natural space station is that in the immediate future man may establish artificial stations to circle the earth at various altitudes. The idea of space stations is not one which was conceived by the present generation. The concept goes back to the turn of the twentieth century.

The first published account of the space station concept appeared in 1897 when Kurt Lasswitz, in a

German science fiction novel entitled "Auf Zwei Planeten," proposed a station some 4000 miles above the North Pole of the earth. Lasswitz wrote of Martians using such a station to observe the earth; and from this point of vantage most of the populated portions of Europe, North America, and Asia would be visible.

That this proposal violated the laws of physics as we understand them is not at issue. What is important is that even that long ago a vehicle high above the earth was conceived and its utilitarian purposes explored.

In 1923 Professor Hermann Oberth proposed a satellite station as an experimental laboratory. Oberth looked ahead to the time when man could get into atmosphereless space where gravity was balanced by centrifugal forces. With the wide range of temperatures available there he considered this an incomparable laboratory. However, the significance of the space station as a refueling point was not stressed by Oberth. This was to be proposed by Dr. Guido von Pirquet.

Von Pirquet realized that a trip from the earth to another planet or the moon meant that the rocket must attain escape velocity—7 miles a second. However, if the trip to the moon or the planets was undertaken from a space station which had already been endowed with a speed of 5 miles a second, then only two miles a second was needed to get away to these distant objectives. This two miles a second was easily attainable with conventional chemical rocket systems.

In the early 1930's the scene shifted from central Europe to England. There an energetic and astute group formed a society which eventually became the British Interplanetary Society. Its members were young men with new, fresh ideas. From this group— before the beginning of World War II—came many original ideas both for space stations and multi-stage rockets to establish them.

With the outbreak of the war most of these speculations were laid aside to be resumed after the war, but again there was a shift in scene. This time the United States "got into the act," for after the war there was a tremendous influx of German rocket scientists and specialists. A few years ago a national magazine featured an article on a tremendous space station proposed and detailed by Dr. Wernher von Braun, the former Technical Director of the German Peenemunde Rocket Station. With the proposal by von Braun, there immediately issued a rash of schemes for putting a station in space and using it as the finest laboratory that man has ever conceived; it could be an incomparable area for scientific research.

The von Braun concept is the "doughnut." As in the case of its predecessors, the trick of spinning the station on its hub or central axis would simulate the force of gravity. The spinning will set up a centrifugal force in which the direction up will be toward the hub while down will be the outside of the doughnut. If the station is considered a bicycle tire, the personnel in the station will be walking on the inside of the tread of the tire.

How fast should the station be spun? To build up the centrifugal force to just balance the gravitational field on the surface of the earth, the 250-foot doughnut must circle once in 12.3 seconds. While it is advisable to simulate a gravitational field, it may be that the spinning at the above rate is too fast. Experience may indicate that a synthetic gravity a third or less of that of the earth may be sufficient to permit normal actions in the space station.

The doughnut will be majestic in size. It may be 250 feet in diameter and the tire 30 feet thick. The tremendous size of the ring will permit it to be divided into three floors to house the various sections of the space station colony. It will be compartmented to insure that disaster does not overtake the entire group if a meteor strikes the space station. Tunnels or spokes will connect the ring with the hub of the station to permit the hub to be used as an entry port. For this, the hub may be spun in the opposite direction to make it stationary relative to an approaching ferry ship from the earth.

The distance of the space station from the earth has been carefully chosen. At an altitude of 1075 miles, the station moves in a two-hour orbit. Because this is divisible into 24 hours of the day, the space station will circle the earth 12 times daily. There are distinct advantages for having the station circle in an even fraction of a day. This means that the station will pass over a given point of the earth moving in the same direction twice a day at predictable times. There are certain uses which the scientists foresee in space stations which dictate the frequency with which the station must pass over a given point. The use will determine the altitude and in turn determine the period of the space station.

The orientation of the space station with respect to the equator of the earth is also of paramount importance for certain studies. Von Braun has chosen the polar orbit which makes certain that the station will pass over a given area at a given time. However, there is one factor which indicates that a single station will not do but a multiplicity of stations will be necessary. As the earth swings around the sun, the axis of the earth being tilted to its path around the sun makes the north pole of the earth tip toward and away from the sun. The space station must maintain its position in space, which means that the station will swing 23½ degrees to one side of the north pole of the earth at one time, and six months later swing to the other side of the sun. Thus, for certain observations a single station will not be satisfactory.

While the doughnut concept of the space station is the classical one, there are others with considerable merit. Others may also provide the advantages of the doughnut and, in addition, include other factors which will aid in the establishment and the maintenance of the station.

The space station must be a home for human beings. There are certain criteria which must be met to consider the design successful. An oxygen-rich atmosphere with a pressure of at least 6 or 7 pounds per square inch is essential. Temperature control must be available to keep the space station livable. The space station must be gas tight to prevent the atmosphere from escaping. It must provide storage space for supplies and equipment. These are the essentials. How do we wrap a structure around them to form a space station?

First of all, we must realize that as the space station must contain an atmosphere, this gas dictates certain principles. A gas is composed of extremely small particles called molecules, which move with speeds up to several miles a second, depending on their mass and temperature. As these particles strike the walls of a container, they tend to push it outward. This outward pressure is the same in all directions, tending to make the container a sphere. Even with a pressure of seven pounds per square inch—which is about half normal pressure at sea level—the outward pressure in even a small container must be many tons. Thus, if it is desired to use a container which is not spherical in shape, the walls must be heavier than for a spherical container. This is objectionable because of the increased weight.

A spherical container, therefore, is the optimum shape for a space station. However, if the volume of a sphere is not big enough for the scientist, the trick is not to make a larger sphere. The ingenious approach is to use several spheres to house the necessary personnel and equipment.

With this philosophy, three or four spheres could be used to make up a complete station. Let's choose four as the number of spheres we want. This means we could link the four spheres in a hollow square with a walkway between the spheres. If each sphere were connected to each of the other spheres, there would be three walkways to each sphere. Two would go to the adjacent spheres and one to the center. In the center, a hub could be built. The space station could be spun around this center to simulate the force of gravity.

In other concepts of space stations, it is deemed necessary to contain all supplies within the spheres. In this concept, the supplies can be stored in the walkways and kept outside the living quarters. The spheres themselves could be smaller and thus the leakage of the atmosphere through the walls would be reduced.

A sphere represents a good shape for an observing

station. If we could use a periscope through the top of one of the spheres we could see more than half the sky. A periscope looking out of the bottom could see the other half of the sky. Thus, from a single sphere, the entire sky would be visible. Because a sphere presents the greatest volume for the least area, it assumes a superior shape as far as meteors are concerned. The shape decreases the potential danger to the occupants in the space station. There is considerable merit in this concept.

Perhaps the most ambitious and comprehensive concept for the space station is the design advanced by Darrell C. Romick. His idea is novel in that the entire third stage of the rocket system which will achieve the desired orbit is used in the construction of the space station. While in the other proposals only a fraction of the total weight going into orbit is to be used for the space station, this concept uses all 35 tons of the third stage rocket as material from which to construct the station.

The proposal has as its objectives the immediate, safe living quarters for personnel arriving in orbit; capability of continual growth of the space station; simplicity of erection; and, finally, construction of the largest possible structure with the minimum quantity of material leaving the earth.

The last is of extreme importance when it is considered that a 7000-ton rocket must be launched to put 35 tons into the sky. It means that for every pound of payload 200 pounds of fuel and hardware must be used to get it up there. At present-day fig-ures, this costs about $20,000. a ton for the payload. One fact must be kept in mind in computing these costs: as the state of the art advances the cost will drop and, given a technological breakthrough, this drop will be precipitous.

The third stage of the rocket will be a cylindrical affair comprising the basic satellite unit. Everything that goes into the space station will evolve from it.

The ferry rockets, once in orbit, will be lined up end to end. The material from the wings, plus curved members carried as cargo, will be used to complete a cylinder nine feet in diameter and twice the length of the ferry rocket. This, as in the case of the ferry rocket, will be compartmented so the crew will have suitable living quarters.

Other ferry rockets will be added until the cylinder is several hundred feet long, made up of perhaps a dozen ferry ships. This first phase should take about two weeks.

The second phase begins with the erection of a giant wheel which will provide synthetic gravity. This is to be 40 feet thick with a diameter of 500 feet. When completed, it will weigh 750 tons and have a volume of 7,500,000 cubic feet.

The rotation rate will govern the force of gravity in the wheel. While it appears that $\frac{1}{4}g$ will bring order out of chaos, in order to be certain it may be best to use ½g. For this the wheel will be spun three revolutions per minute.

At the same time the wheel is under construction, the nine-foot cylinder made from the ferry rocket becomes the kernel of a still larger cylinder 75 feet in diameter and 940 feet in length, with a final weight of 250 tons. It would be composed of three separate cells with a total volume of 4,000,000 cubic feet. This cylinder will not revolve, thus providing the gravity-free portion of the space laboratory. When the second phase is completed at the end of the fourth month, the personnel will be provided with all the comforts of home. At this point, the space station will become an efficient operation capable of performing desired functions. Also at this point, the leisurely construction of the third phase can get underway.

There is no urgency in the completion of this phase. It will take over six years to accomplish. When finished, the cylinder will have grown to a diameter of 1000 feet. Its length will be over a half mile with dome-shaped ends.

The 500-foot wheel will grow until it is 1500 feet in diameter and will be set spinning at one revolution per minute—the speed of the second hand on a clock. The total volume will be approximately 3,-000,000,000 cubic feet!

This is by far the most ambitious project ever developed to put an observation platform in the sky; but, in time, even more revolutionary ideas are bound to put in an appearance. Let's discuss one which at the moment can be considered only a wild dream; but it is a dream based on physical principles well understood.

Suppose at some future date, when nuclear power has been harnessed to provide motive power in space, we were to take a large space ship to the region of the asteroids. Would it be possible to capture one of the several thousand bodies now moving between Mars and Jupiter and bring it close to the earth as a captured space station? These bodies are made of rock and iron, and range in size from a few hundred feet to 400 miles. However, it is certain that thousands of other smaller bodies also exist out there in this belt.

The dream envisions a plan whereby a power unit would push against one of these ready-made space platforms so that its present path around the sun would be gradually shifted until the earth's gravitational field could snare it. After that, it would orbit around the earth. There would be a change in masters; the earth, curiously, would adopt one of the sun's children for its own.

A 500-foot asteroid is so massive and the power plant to move it would be so small that the rocket exhaust must be endowed with tremendous speeds—perhaps ten miles a second—to create significant force. At the moment this is an unheard-of speed, but these speculations have a habit of becoming reality. Let us assume that this speed will be available; how do we use it?

The asteroid has an enormous amount of material in it. An asteroid 500 feet in diameter would "weigh" about 6 million tons. At the earth's distance from the sun, this would move with a speed of 18 miles a second. If we assume that we must go beyond the orbit of Mars to pick up the asteroid, it might possess an orbital speed of 12 miles a second. This would mean that a mass of 6 million tons must have its speed and direction of motion changed to permit the earth to capture it.

Even with nuclear power, this is extremely difficult. We must have material to shoot out the back as exhaust. It may be possible to "cannibalize" the asteroid to provide the mass. The fuel for the power plant we will assume will last for years, so it will need no replenishing.

Now for the mechanics of capturing the asteroid. The continuous operation of the nuclear rockets will impress on the asteroid a steady force, slowly changing its speed in a new direction which would ultimately make it the earth's captive. Knowing the thrust of the power plant and the mass and speed of the asteroid, it can be shown how much the exerted force will affect the asteroid. By equating the intensity of the two forces, one for the asteroid and the other for the power plant, the time for the change in orbit can be computed.

Astronomers can predict the motion of these bodies, knowing the forces acting on them. These computations can be monitored at regular intervals to check the asteroid's position, and with the giant computers a continuous solution may be available to compare with the computed solution. In computing this progress, even the perturbative effects of the planets and the moon may be taken into consideration. The accelerations applied to the asteroid may continue perhaps for several decades. The continuous solution will also indicate predicted positions, so that the one horrendous possibility of the asteroid colliding with the earth may be avoided. Changes in the orbit can be made to forestall any possibility of this type.

Once the asteroid has been captured, it can be set spinning to provide a centrifugal field to help the scientists stationed there. Under this simulated gravity condition, the personnel would have to live on the inside shell of the asteroid or on plastic floors covering excavations in the asteroid. What is even more important, it may provide a storehouse of raw material for use in space without investing 200 pounds of fuel and hardware for every pound of material put into an orbit.

Recently there has been a suggestion that a space station is an outmoded concept. Some scientists would like to bypass the entire space station and head directly for the moon. They realize that a tremendous amount of power would be necessary to go directly from the earth to the moon and land a manned craft there. With nuclear rockets the direct descent on the moon is a possibility, but it is a fantastically difficult undertaking. For that reason, it is believed that the scientists will put a space station in the sky first and head for the moon from that point, rather than attempt the direct moon landing. The assembling of a space station from materials sent into the sky at different times is difficult enough. To have the material rendezvous with what has already been established means that direction and cutoff speed of the ferry rockets must be precise, and the timing perfect. However, it is felt that this is much simpler than taking the giant step of putting a man on the moon from the surface of the earth.

CHAPTER 8

The Observatory in Space

Astronomers have peered through a shimmering gauze-like veil ever since man first turned his eyes to the sky. The veil is the ocean of atmosphere which absorbs, scatters, and attenuates the very radiations which are the clue-bearing messengers to help us solve the mysteries of the universe.

Because the atmosphere is in a turbulent state, images of celestial objects wander over small areas of the photographic plate, smearing out the details. Except from observatories in excellent locations, on rare fine nights of "good seeing," images of the planets squirm when seen through a telescope much like objects viewed above a hot stove or a radiator. Our sky by day is blue because the particles of our air are of just the right size and number to scatter the blue light strongly. This light from the stars and other celestial objects is scattered by night, as well, and produces a general blue background illumination which the eye seldom notes—except when a bright moon is above the horizon—but which is readily "seen" by the photographic plate. The general background illumination limits the length of exposure that can be made; therefore, many very faint objects will remain forever undiscoverable by photography from the surface of the earth, no matter how large we may build our telescopes.

An observatory in space will not eliminate all of our problems. For example, in addition to starlight scattered by the particles of our air, a general background illumination accounting for about 60% of the total comes from the zodiacal light, as we call the scattered sunlight from the particles of a great lens-shaped dust cloud centered on the sun. We believe that we shall need to get out about as far as Jupiter is from the sun before we shall be free of this glow. Another disadvantage of a space observatory is the strong probability that we shall be unable to use our familiar photographic processes, just as we have succeeded in bringing them to a very high stage of efficiency and versatility. At the earth's surface, because of the very screening effects of the atmosphere that we so much deplore, the ultraviolet and other short-wave radiations are not able to spoil our pictures; in space, the intensities of these radiations are such that, long before our desired picture can be registered, the unwanted radiations will have fogged the emulsion. We shall be forced to depend on various TV-type electronic scanners that will accept the radiations we want and reject those we do not wish to register. Significant advances must be made in these devices before they will be suitable; today they cannot deliver as finely detailed images as even the common types of photographic emulsions can produce.

Despite these difficulties, which are certain to be overcome in time at least to some degree, an observatory in space will contribute enormously to advances in our knowledge of the universe. Certainly one of the most significant studies will be that of the sun and its effects on the earth. The sun is the nearest star—only 93,000,000 miles distant. The next nearest star, one that we cannot see from mid-northern latitudes, is 275,000 times as far away. The stars are so distant that no telescope in the world can reveal them as anything but points of light except under special conditions where interferometric observations are the goal. In photographs, some stars appear larger than others, but this is a spurious effect; the light of a brighter star spreads farther through the photographic emulsion, to produce a larger spot. Curiously, the larger the telescope the smaller the star images, but all of them will appear brighter. We can learn much about the stars, but many things about them we shall be able to surmise only as a result of intimate knowledge of the sun.

If the light of the sun or a star is passed through a prism, like a chandelier crystal of triangular cross section, the light will be spread out into a smear of color, ranging from deepest red at one end to deep violet at the other, with orange, yellow, green, and blue falling between these extremes. This smear of color is called the spectrum of the source of the light. If a slit and a couple of lenses are arranged around this prism, to make what the scientist calls a spectroscope, the colors are more purely seen and, for most sources such as the sun and the stars, there will be dark lines of various intensities crossing the spectrum.

The relative intensities of the various colors of the spectrum and the positions of the dark lines give us a wealth of information about the source of the light. We can consider the pattern of the dark lines as the fingerprint of the composition of the source, because only certain lines are produced by certain atoms, and no other atom produces the same lines, just as no two people have the same set of fingerprints. The reason that the lines are dark is that the atoms steal a little of the light of the sun's interior layers.

The spectrum of a star such as the sun can reveal the temperature, the density, the composition, the motion, and many other properties of the star. But some of our information is only approximate, and much that is carried by the full gamut of radiations of the star never reaches us. The ozone in our atmosphere absorbs almost all of the radiations beyond the deepest visible violet—the ultraviolet, the X-rays, the gamma rays that we know the sun and other stars must emit. Water vapor and carbon dioxide attenuate the radiations in the long wavelength region, and certain ionized layers in the atmosphere are opaque to the deep regions of the radio waves, except for a "window" through which today we are just beginning to examine the universe with radio telescopes.

Some investigators consider it remarkable that our eyes are sensitive to just that octave of light from deep red to deep violet which gets through our atmosphere so handily. It is certainly not a coincidence; man has evolved on earth with this band of light falling on him, and his eyes have become adapted to this kind of radiation. In the laboratory, he has extended the range of sensitivity of his eyes by means of photographic emulsions sensitive to the short wavelengths, and through the use of various types of receptors for the long wavelengths. But these, except for the radio telescopes, are of little avail when he raises these "eyes" to the stars.

But imagine what can be done when the astronomer can establish an observatory in a space station. There, above the atmosphere, all radiations will arrive little changed from the time they left their sources and, particularly in the ultraviolet and down to the short X-rays, we shall be able to fill in some very important gaps in our knowledge even of the composition of the sun, our nearest star. The spectrum lines of some of our light-weight abundant elements lie in this region and can be observed only under unusual and critical conditions. Not only the compositions of the surface layers of the stars but even the shaky theories we now have concerning the interiors of the stars, and their evolution, may be resolved when we can examine the short wavelength region of an undiluted spectrum.

Cataclysmic outbursts are recorded in the sky, as some stars literally "blow their tops" and emit for brief periods truly fantastic amounts of energy. We call these exploding stars *novae* and *supernovae*. The ordinary novae flare up to temporary brightnesses of from 10,000 to half a million times their previous brightnesses, before fading more slowly back to approximately their original conditions. Some of the supernovae give off in a day as much energy as the sun emits in a million years! While many theories have been proposed to account for these outbursts, the astronomer possesses no definitive information as to their causes and exact nature. Perhaps, in time, by exploring the entire range of radiations emanating from the stars, we shall reveal the mechanisms for these outbursts.

The distribution of the stars is one of the fundamental problems in astronomy. Our sun lies in one of the inner arms of the spiral galaxy we call the Milky Way System. Throughout the system is finely-divided matter in the form of dust and gases, spread non-uniformly but confined more or less to the same general plane of the disklike galaxy of stars. Our census of the stars and the general shape and size of the system of which the sun is a member is conditioned by the distribution of this obscuring material. While observations from a space station will not permit the sweeping aside of this obscuring veil, we shall at least have access to the full range of radiations of the stars, and perhaps we shall be able to make our investigations with some wavelength that almost if not entirely penetrates the dust and gas clouds.

Today we believe that fully half of the matter in our observable universe is in the form of unorganized material—the tiny, primitive particles of dust, gases and atoms both whole and shattered.* The ratio of this free, unattached material to that found in the stars will be studied from a space observatory. This is most important research, because these giant gas and dust clouds are considered to be the stellar incubators where stars are literally born. We believe that we have seen stars born in our time, particularly in the Great Nebula in Orion.

* Astronomers have recently uncovered evidence which indicates that the amount of material in these nebulae has been overestimated by perhaps as much as 100 times.

Dr. Lyman Spitzer of Princeton and Dr. Fred L. Whipple of Harvard and the Smithsonian Astrophysical Observatory believe that investigations in the ultraviolet, from a space observatory, may be able to give us the information we desperately seek about the compositions and constitutions of these dark clouds, as well as of all diffuse matter between the planets and between the stars. If we pursue this problem far enough, we shall perhaps learn how the chemical elements originated and evolved, and then we may be able to go on to the even more intriguing problem of the origin of the universe itself.

Today, two rival theories of the origin and evolution of the universe struggle for recognition and acceptance. One is the "big boom" idea, in which the universe began some five or so billion years ago as the result of the explosion of a giant "atom." Opposed to this is the "continuous creation" theory of a group of British astrophysicists led by Bondi and Gold. From a space observatory, some clue may be discovered that will indicate which of these two lines of reasoning (or perhaps some other) is more compatible with the observations.

There exists a strange category of star known as the "white dwarf," incredibly dense and certainly peculiar in its internal constitution. Most of these stars are very faint, not only intrinsically but also because of their distances. They may be much more numerous than we suspect, and a space observatory may permit us not only to find more of them but also to decide whether they are, as some have supposed, "collapsed stars" near the ends of their lives.

Coming closer to home, we find that the planets of our own solar system hide many of their secrets behind our atmosphere. Some of these bodies possess their own atmospheres and sunlight, penetrating these gaseous envelopes to some degree, and contaminated by their materials before being reflected to us on earth. Our own atmosphere additionally contaminates this light on its way to us at the surface, and the lines in the final spectrum that are due to our atmosphere's materials are disentangled from those due to the planetary atmospheres only with great difficulty. Before any trips are taken to these other bodies in space, we must have as complete a story as possible concerning the compositions and densities of the planetary atmospheres.

The nearest body is, of course, the moon, which we are sure possesses no atmosphere in the ordinary sense. This factor concerning our only known natural satellite at least will not surprise us when we get there (see Chapter 11). But Mars and Venus—certainly the bodies that we shall set our space ship sights on when we have established a base on the moon—have many secrets from us (see Chapter 14). We know that Mars has an atmosphere and that there is more carbon dioxide in it, over each square mile of the planet, than there is in our atmosphere on earth. There must be at least a little free oxygen there, and water vapor, but we can't detect them, nor can we find out whether the major constituent of the Martian atmosphere is nitrogen, argon, or a mixture of both. We know that the dense atmosphere of Venus contains much carbon dioxide, but beyond that we know nothing, although we suspect much and many varied things about that envelope. From an observatory in space we shall be able to find definitive answers to these questions, so important to the future of space travel.

So far, this chapter has been devoted, appropriately, to the brief discussion of some of the reasons why we should look forward to the early establishment of an observatory in space. Now it is time to see how it can be done.

The earth is a very massive body, hence it possesses a large amount of inertia; it is difficult to move it. A small child can push a chair or table across the floor, but no matter how much a grown man may jump up and down on the earth, the earth does not change its state of motion appreciably. Our telescopes are very large and massive and, as we move them, the earth acts as a stable platform. In space, a platform will need to have stability of a high order before it can serve as a base for a telescope.

Let's imagine for a moment that an astronomer in a space suit steps from a space platform to point a telescope at a star. As he tries to move the telescope, there will be a reaction to his effort, and he will move, also. Even standing on the space platform, the weightlessness of the astronomer will impose a considerable difficulty in trying to point a telescope. If the telescope is mounted rigidly in gimbal supports on the space platform, an attempt to rotate the telescope to a new position will result in some degree of rotation of the space platform, depending on its inertia as compared with that of the telescope itself.

The space platform must be stabilized artificially, and today there are in existence or in advanced stages of development stabilization systems of many kinds, some of them actually depending on keeping the space station always aligned in a certain direction with respect to a given star. Such an arrangement would be ideal for an observatory in space, although its accomplishment lies somewhat in the category of "which came first? The chicken or the egg?" We have been discussing the difficulty of pointing a telescope at a star, from a space platform, and now we think of stabilizing the platform by pointing a telescope at a star.

An unmanned platform would be difficult to maneuver into stability of this nature, but it could be done. A manned platform could more or less easily be maneuvered so that a fixed telescope could be pointed at a star, thus orienting the platform in one direction, at least. It would be necessary, however, to have two such fixed telescopes, directed to two predetermined stars, in order to stabilize the platform completely. Once the platform is in orbit (probably it would be assembled in orbit), small rocket jets can rotate it this way or that until the orientation conditions are met.

Such stabilization systems are coupled with rocket jets or compressed gas jets that automatically turn on to correct any deviations from the desired orientation. Such systems are not too different from the automatic guiding systems used on some large telescopes. No matter how smooth the bearings or accurate the mechanism that turns a telescope on earth to follow a star as the earth rotates, small errors occur. A little of the light of the star is stolen and is fed to a photoelectric cell arrangement, which actuates the proper motor to keep the star always as nearly as possible centered in the telescope's field of view. A very minor alteration of such a system would suffice for the automatic maintenance of the orientation of a space platform, no matter how much its orbit might precess or otherwise change in the course of time.

Now that we have provided for a stable base for the telescope, what of the instrument itself? Because of the weightlessness in space, the instrument need not be massive, like those on earth. The 200-inch mirror of the Hale telescope on Palomar Mountain weighs almost 15 tons! The total weight of the giant telescope is 500 tons only because the structure must be strong and rigid enough to prevent bending of the telescope to destroy its efficiency as an optical instrument. In space, the same heavy mirror could be held by a spider of light aluminum or magnesium structural members, whose only function would be to make sure that the optical elements remain correctly aligned.

No astronomer would think of taking a 200-inch mirror weighing 15 tons into space, even if it could easily be done and there were room in the ferry rocket for the purpose. The only reason for the weight of the mirror on earth is to give it the rigidity it needs to prevent warping under the influence of gravity, as it is tilted to different positions. The optical surface of the mirror must remain at all times as nearly as possible the same precise figure that was designed and ground into it. In space, the warping due to gravity will be absent. The ideal mirror could then be a thin glass plate with little weight, that could be transported to the space station.

For certain work with the telescope, appropriate filters may be able to protect the photographic plates from fogging by unwanted short-wave radiations in the ultraviolet and X-ray regions. We are assisted somewhat in this by the fact that mirrors do not very efficiently reflect these short waves; indeed, if we wish to pick these up, we shall need to devise some scheme in which the incoming radiations barely graze the mirror surface, thus imposing a very complicated optical problem not yet tackled on earth. But the situation in space is different; not only must we filter these unwanted radiations in some of the work, but we must make sure that the penetrating X-rays and gamma rays cannot get at the photographic plates even from the back or sides, as well as the front.

It is probable that electronic systems, and not normal optical ones, will be used. The image will be scanned as in our TV systems, after considerable modification has been effected in our existing systems. Appropriate monitors will be at the disposal of the astronomer at the space platform, but the information will also be transmitted to earth in the form of electronic impulses, there to be photographed for permanent record. A permanent record can be simultaneously stored at the space station in the form of videotape that, periodically, can be sent back to earth by ferry rocket or by some other re-entry device.

There will undoubtedly be complicated problems of shielding this electronic equipment from the bombardment of particles and radiations in space. The magnetic tape for recording the video response of the telescope may be altered by these space radiations in time. Much research in this field must be conducted before this materializes.

One protection we must surely provide is against temperature changes. In full sunlight the temperature of the components of the telescope system will be enormously higher than when the satellite is in the shadow of the earth, and the natural expansion of metals and other materials will produce distortions far greater than those we experience in our instruments on earth, where the atmosphere tends to smooth out the contrast between daytime and nighttime temperatures. It is imperative that some form of shield be used to shelter the instrument when it is in direct sunlight.

Micrometeoroids will bombard the optical and other surfaces. It is likely that after a relatively short time the optical surfaces, pitted by these small particles, will seem to have been sandblasted. There appears to be no cure for this hazard; only refinishing the optical surfaces will restore the telescope to a usable condition.

While such a space observatory for serious and prolonged research could be established, it is unlikely that it will be. By the time it can be built and operated, other great events will probably render it unnecessary. It is more likely that more or less ordinary satellites with small telescopes—perhaps no larger than those owned or even made by amateur astronomers—will be used, not at all completely stabilized, to test the optical-electronic systems; the TV-type scanners will send their impulses to earth for direct viewing and photographing. The first real space observatory will probably be on the moon.

Except for the problem of orientation and stabilization, all that has been discussed earlier in this chapter will apply to an observatory on the moon. As on the earth, however, provision must be made on the moon for guiding the telescope to follow a star or other object as the moon rotates on its axis and performs its other motions. Again, however, automatic following devices actuated by photocells can accomplish a fantastically accurate job, to give us in a brief interval information that we could never obtain from our great telescopes on earth. The surface gravity on the moon is one-sixth of that on earth, but this departure from the weightlessness of a space platform is only a small penalty to pay for permanence and extreme stability.

Small telescopes may be sent up in unmanned satellites or operated from space stations in the next few years. Then man will reach the moon and, shortly after, establish some kind of working colony there. As one part of that establishment, an astronomical observatory should be set up and operated. We can afford to wait that long when we realize what we shall learn from it.

CHAPTER 9

Hazards in Space

There are many complaints about the growing travel hazards on earth; but in space, where there are no trolley-car jams, no Sunday drivers, no hot-rods nor road hogs, there exist still more hazards than are to be found during the rush hours on our busiest main street. And the consequences of not being able to combat these hazards will be far more serious; in fact, we may say that they will almost always be fatal.

In space, beyond the protective atmosphere of the earth, all the lethal radiations found in nature will beset the traveler unless he is properly protected. Earth's air acts as a shield to burn out the tiny bits of cosmic debris that dash through space, and it acts to convert into less harmful forms the radiations and atomic particles that shower the top of the atmosphere.

In space, the traveler must live always in some form of air-proof, escape-proof prison. He must do something about the noxious gases and other poisons that he himself generates. When the rockets cease firing, he will find himself in a weird, out-of-this-world, gravity-free condition in which every motion will be a challenge to the most delicate mechanism of the body—the nervous system. And even before he reaches this strange gravity-free condition he may be subjected to brutal, crushing accelerations which would tax the finest physical specimen to the very limit of his endurance. These, then, are some of the hazards that await man as he ventures off the earth to explore space.

Beyond the atmosphere the whole gamut of radiations, from the long radio waves to the short-wave, high-energy gamma and X-rays, will shower any space vehicle. Actually, the long-wave radiations will not be dangerous, we believe, although at present there is some feeling that perhaps human beings react adversely to certain radar waves. The great fear is that the short-wave radiations will damage and perhaps injure seriously the traveler in space. At the moment we do not know enough about the actions of these radiations on animal tissues to be able to draw a definitive picture.

When the radiation spectrum is analyzed, we find

that the radiations to fear are those of shorter wave-length than those of visible light. Even our life-giving, life-saving atmosphere transmits some of the ultraviolet radiation, to produce sunburn. As these lines are being written, the author is very well aware of this ability of radiations because of an indiscreet procedure while fishing. But the ultraviolet radiation that gave the writer his burn is as nothing compared to that which lies in the shorter wavelength region. Beyond the ultraviolet that in some measure pene-trates the earth's atmosphere we find the ultra-short ultraviolet, the X-rays, and the gamma radiation.

Even a sheet of paper will stop almost all of the ultraviolet, so in a space ship or even in a space suit outside the ship these radiations should present no problems. A space suit made of a leaded cloth can absorb at least some of the X-rays and so protect the traveler from injury. Much more protection would be necessary against the gamma rays.

The real hazard, however, may be the primary cos-mic rays. The stars, including our sun, throw off ionized atoms of hydrogen, helium, carbon, and other elements which develop tremendous energies in passing through space; these are the cosmic "rays," so-called.

Many readers may ask a question like this: What is this nonsense about the danger of cosmic rays when I have seen them recorded by a geiger counter on earth? The question is a legitimate one, but the readers do not realize that cosmic rays are of two general types. One type is the primary cosmic "ray," with tremendously high energy, found out in space; we have just mentioned those. They are the primary cosmic rays. The ones we receive on the earth's surface are the secondaries, some of them being actual radiations, others atomic particles of various kinds. They are produced from the impacts of primary cosmic rays on air particles at altitudes of perhaps 25 miles. The primary rays possess about a million times as much energy as the secondaries. We have evolved under secondary cosmic rays, and in fact there is a strong belief that these may have played a significant role in the evolution of man to his present level. They no longer can harm us. But when we get above 25 miles and enter the region of the primary cosmic rays it is conceivable that without sufficient protection we may be seriously harmed.

The exact nature of the hazard is unknown at the moment, although biologists believe that the strong ionizing action of these primary cosmic rays may break up cells which, when they try to reproduce or to repair themselves, will not have proper mating of the chromosomes, thus giving rise to mutations and to malignancies. Certainly there is good reason, the geneticists tell us, for apprehension concerning the actions on tissues, from these cosmic rays. It is, however, this writer's firm belief that, even if the primary cosmic rays prove very harmful, it will not necessarily

mean that space travel will not materialize. There
will be too many adventurers who will risk these
hazards and go anyway, and there is always the possibility that shielding can be provided.

There are other tiny particles also presenting dangers to the space traveler—the space shrapnel found
throughout the solar system and perhaps, although
most certainly to a reduced degree, even outside the
system. From a dark place of observation, look up
into the sky intently and continuously on a clear
night. Several times in a single hour you will find a
streak cutting across the sky—a shooting star or falling star, familiarly, but a meteor to the astronomer.
Actually it is not a star, a big thing like our sun, a
million times the volume of the earth. These meteors
are tiny bits of matter, in most instances no larger
than a grain of sand.

Dr. Fletcher G. Watson, in his book *Between the
Planets,* estimates that at least a billion meteoroids
that produce meteors of the 8th magnitude or
brighter enter the earth's atmosphere every day. We
call the object in space a meteoroid (a very tiny one
might be called a micrometeoroid or micrometeorite); if the object enters the atmosphere and produces
a visible streak of light, we call that phenomenon a
meteor; if a portion of it survives its flaming flight
and lands on the earth, perhaps to be picked up and
displayed in a museum, we call it a meteorite. Some
of the micrometeorites enter the atmosphere, but—

because their masses are so low as compared with their surface areas—they can be slowed down sufficiently not to be consumed. These may be the source of the definitely meteoritic dust that is found in the drain water from roof tops and even in dredgings from the depths of the seas. They may also furnish the nuclei for much of the earth's rain.

An 8th-magnitude meteor is mentioned in the preceding paragraph. This is too faint to be seen with the unaided eye; it would need to be at least 15 times brighter to be seen. According to Dr. Watson's estimate, five meteors enter each square mile of the earth's atmosphere each day, which means that each square foot of the atmosphere receives a meteoroid each 15,200 years—one sufficient to produce a meteor of 8th magnitude or brighter. Certainly many more of smaller size or slower speed also shower our atmosphere.

Most meteoroids do not survive to reach the earth's surface; less than 2,000 meteorites have been found, although undoubtedly many thousands of others lie undiscovered in the seas, as well as on land. We do not suffer from the bombardment of these celestial bullets. But in space a stationary vehicle with a cross-section of 3,000 square feet would be struck by a meteoroid of 8th-magnitude size each two or three years. In the recent ascent of the "Pioneer" moon-shoot by the U. S. Air Force, out to 79,000 miles and return in about 42 hours, two micrometeorite impacts were recorded on detecting surfaces totaling only a square foot or so; undoubtedly these objects were of almost microscopic size.

Overcoming the effects of the impacts by these space bullets has occupied the attention of many scientists. Some would equip space ships with "missile bumpers." These would be thin shells completely enclosing the vehicle, to absorb the shock of the meteoroids. The result of a collision would be an almost instantaneous vaporization of both the meteoroid and the spot of the shell where the hit occurred; since the energy of the particle would thus be absorbed, the collision would not damage the ship.

However, we must not overlook the fact that there are large meteoroids and, if one of them should strike the space ship and penetrate the hull, the passengers would be in serious trouble. We might arrange that space suits will be worn at all times and that any sudden decrease in pressure in the ship will automatically cause the suits to inflate. But for eating and for other vital functions it is conceivable that the suits would be discarded and, if a hit should occur then, there would be a possibility of catastrophe.

Let us assume that a means has been devised for quickly closing up a hole in the ship, as in a submarine where leaking plates sprung by depth bomb concussion are soon stopped up. Normally, only about half of normal atmospheric pressure will be carried in a space ship, so let us assume that the pressure falls from about six pounds per square inch to one pound per square inch. Will there be time to plug up the hole produced by the collision?

In a fraction of a second, every last bit of air in the lungs will escape as in an explosive sneeze. The lungs then will fill with carbon dioxide and water, and the unfortunate space traveler will drown in his own vapors. And this will not take long; the action would be well on its way in the first half-minute. Moreover, there is another unpleasant effect. With the loss in pressure, the moisture beneath the skin will begin to vaporize and bubble; some space medicine doctors believe that even the blood would begin to boil at this low pressure. Thus there will be several unwholesome results of being in a compartment of a space ship punctured by a meteoroid.

So far, we have blithely spoken of the hazards to man after he gets into space, and we haven't worried too much about getting him there. To escape from the earth in the most economical way means that we should burn our fuel rapidly so that energy will not be wasted in lifting unburned fuel. Under these conditions, accelerations become quite high with our chemical rockets. Someday we may have nuclear-powered rockets (see Chapter 4) with much more energy, and will be able to take off from earth with much lower accelerations, but let's consider what happens as very high accelerations are experienced.

In Johnsville, about 15 miles north of Philadelphia, there is a huge, modernistic, reinforced concrete blockhouse—the U. S. Navy Aviation Medical Acceleration Laboratory. Cylindrical in form and austere in appearance, the 130-foot blockhouse has as its prime occupant a giant slingshot called a centrifuge. This is no ordinary slingshot; it is a powerful research tool, designed to whirl human beings around in a dizzy, crushing circle that establishes forces that can literally tear the guts inside a strong and healthy man.

Imagine a condition in which your blood is being forced through your arteries as though pushed by irresistible pistons. Picture your sight dimming and yourself finally going into a blackout. Imagine your stomach, intestines, heart, and lungs bludgeoned downward. And picture your brain being compressed steadily and inexorably into the base of your skull until you lapse into merciful unconsciousness. If you can imagine these punishments, you can visualize what happens inside a pilot when he is subjected to the high accelerative force of many "g's." Surprisingly enough, most of these body distortions are not painful, and pilots are willing to subject themselves repeatedly to high accelerations, despite the temporary keen discomfort.

Just what is a "g"? It is simply the force exerted on the body by the earth's normal gravity. We might think of it as the force resulting from the acceleration of a racing car by 22 miles per hour in a single second, or about three times the highest acceleration of a fine modern stock car.

If you drop a coin to the floor it falls with the acceleration of one g. You can jump off a table and develop many instantaneous g's and not be hurt. The punishment to which a pilot in the centrifuge is subjected is due not only to the accelerative forces but also to the time during which the forces are acting. As an example, Col. John P. Stapp in his rocket-propelled sled on rails was subjected to a deceleration of 40 g's, but only for a fifth of a second as he started his slow-down. If he had undergone such a high deceleration for even a few seconds, the odds for his surviving the experience would have been quite low.

Getting back to the centrifuge, the task of the test personnel there is to put subjects through a grueling, punishing, exciting few seconds in the centrifuge, and then to analyze the data to determine what can be done for pilots who will be subjected to these racking accelerations on a take-off from the earth.

To get a better picture of what is going on in the centrifuge gondola, a movie camera is trained on the subject to record his reactions. A television camera and monitor are in operation to give the control operator and doctor a glimpse of what goes on in the gondola. X-ray pictures of the subject can be taken at the rate of 48 a minute. Special physiological sensing and measuring devices record the pilot's heart rate, respiration, blood pressure, temperature, heart waves, and brain waves. A complete medical record of the pilot under stress is available after the experiment.

In some experiments, rats have been whipped up to 19 g's, then frozen solid by pouring 320-degree-below-zero liquid nitrogen on them. They are then dissected to see how their tissues survived the distended, distorted state due to high accelerations.

At Wright Field and at Johnsville, human guinea pigs have been subjected to the accelerations necessary to put a man into an orbit. They were apparently unaffected by this experience; so, at least for the moment, we can say that the accelerations needed are within the tolerance of pilots today.

One important consideration as yet unmentioned is the experience in vehicle control that can be obtained and developed in the centrifuge, along with the straining to withstand the acceleration effects. It is not enough to be able to come through the take-off accelerations in good physical condition; the space pilot must be able to perform necessary operations—if not during take-off, at least a very short time afterward.

As long as the rocket motors are operating, the passengers will be subject to accelerations and will experience weight. The instant the rocket motors cease firing, the travelers will feel that they are freely

carefully tailored suit will be worn by the first man in space. These
suits will be made of leaded glass fibers for the articulated parts of the
suit and lead platelets to protect the radiation-sensitive parts of the body.

The full moon showing the separation of the moon into two halves in
which the seas predominate in the top or southern half and the "old"
moon predominates in the northern half. The white outline in the southern half shows the encroachment of the seas in this area.

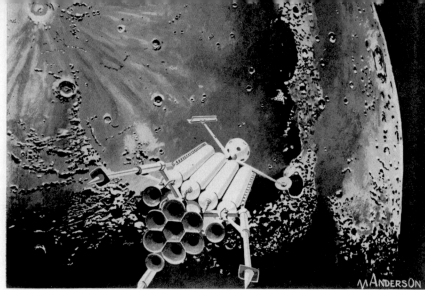

Approach to the moon. The rocket motors will have to fire until "touch down" is actually achieved. Here we see the rocket beginning its turn, so that it will fall to the moon's surface, rocket motors first.

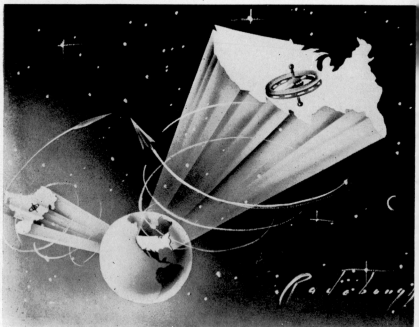

In the past, a nation was master of all the air space over its territory; but with satellites covering scores of countries in a 90-minute period it is obvious that the old laws no longer apply.

Long-lived satellites like the "Baby" Vanguard cannot be given a "voice" to clutter up a radio frequency. Only satellites whose radios can be controlled from the earth will be permitted to go into the sky.

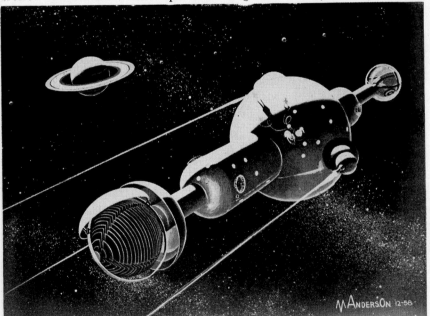

The long-ignored Peltier effect may be used to cool and heat space ships. When a current is passed through two dissimilar metals, heat is generated at one junction while the other remains cold. By using the radiation of the sun to fall on a junction, electric energy can be generated, which in turn can be used in the space ship as a power source.

Using algae, it is possible to regenerate the atmosphere of a space ship and to furnish food for the inhabitants.

If nuclear energy is not available soon, giant balloons may be launched with satellites to provide energy for them. The balloons will be covered with solar cells, and will feed the energy generated by these cells into the instrumentation in the carrier, with the connecting mechanism acting as the power transmission cable.

Our experience with the Atlas satellite in Project SCORE indicates that communications satellites are just around the corner.

Complex machines will be built to mine the moon for the useful materials. The automatic mining machinery will be completely unmanned, except for the observer who will sit in a tower with manual over-rides at his hand.

The X-15 will be man's first challenge to space. When the rocket motors ignite, it will streak straight into the sky, hit a ceiling of over 100 miles and a speed of perhaps 6000 miles per hour.

A low-altitude satellite may pick up an instantaneous picture of the earth to telemeter back to the earth for meteorological interpretation.

returning from a satellite retro-
ckets and parachutes must be used
start the fall and land safely. An
ormous amount of heat must be
sipated in re-entry.

A huge mirror in space may be used in
time for weather modification. While
the mirror cannot concentrate enough
solar energy to create fires or do damage, it *can* concentrate the energy of
the sun on small areas where there is
danger of frost. These mirrors may
aid in evaporating clouds to forestall
continued rain, and may even turn
snow and hail to rain.

e live on the bottom of an ocean
atmosphere which filters, scatters,
d absorbs the body damaging radi-
ions of the sun.

Circling the moon. Lunar satellites will
be a prominent part of space travel.

Assembling the space station. The parts of giant space ships going into orbit around the earth will be cannibalized to furnish the material for the space station.

The young man going into s travel requires a concentrated pe of schooling. He must be more ficient in many more subjects his father. He must begin earl his career—in high school—to pre himself for this great new adven

One of the most severe challenges to which the space man will be subject will be acclimatization to gravity-free space. While many pilots have been subject to this condition for over a half minute, the true test will come when man is subjected to it for at least a 24-hour period.

The Andromeda Galaxy—a star tem of about 100 billion stars, a 2,000,000 light years distant. Ph graphs of this star system taken the largest telescopes can resolv into types of objects found in own Milky Way system.

Resolution of the Andromeda Galaxy. With the 100-inch telescope at the Mt. Wilson Observatory the edges of the galaxy can be broken up into star clouds, both open and closed clusters, nebulae both bright and dark, and finally the cepheid variables which can be used to determine the distances to these objects.

Meteor and comet photograph. While photographing the Brooks comet of 1893, Professor Barnard also caught the meteor moving through the field. These meteors are tiny bits of cosmic debris which move with speeds up to 45 miles a second. The friction with the atmosphere creates a luminous streak many miles in length but only a few feet in diameter. These constitute one of the most serious hazards in space travel.

Nova Herculis photographed on October 2, 1921, and December 24, 1934.
The first one shows the nova as a faint star and the second shows it as i
became one of the twenty brightest stars in the sky.

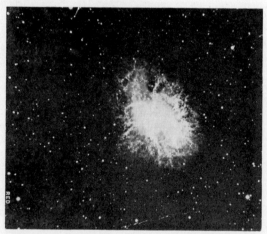

The Crab Nebula. This is the remains of a
supernova which erupted in 1054 A.D. It was
observed by Chinese astronomers at that
time. Only recently have astronomers been
able to identify this nebula as the remains
of the explosion which took place in the 11th
century. Like the nova, the supernova may
provide vital links for the understanding of
the life cycles of the stars.

ar Cloud in Sagittrius. Photographing is part of the sky th a large telescope rmits the registering of this endless mber of stars. The ason for the concenation here is that we e looking at the center of the Milky Way stem. Upon careful spection, small dark obules may be seen mong the stars. Asonomers believe at they are the awning places for e stars, and that ars are born of the rk material making o the globules.

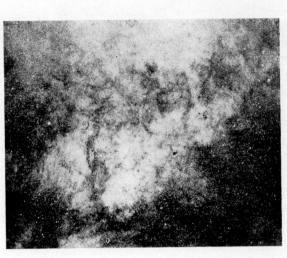

Artist's concept of a settlement on the moon after the year 2000.

The Horsehead Nebula in Orion. In this part of the sky, which is near the plane of the Milky Way, vast quantities of both bright and dark nebula abound. On the right may be seen the sheet of dark nebulosity; on the left we are looking deep into space, and are seeing the faint stars which lie at great distances from the earth.

A cluster of five galaxies of various types in the constellation of Pegasus. Astronomers have discovered that galaxies cluster in groups. Our Milky Way is a member of a system of about seventeen galaxies called the Metagalaxy.

The sun in total eclipse.

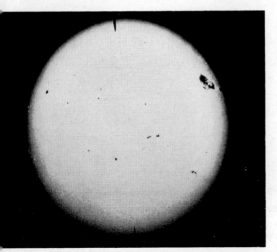

The sun in continuous light. When we observe the sun with a telescope with our eyes properly protected, we can see black areas surrounded by somewhat grayer ones. The black areas are the umbra and the gray areas the penumbra of sunspots.

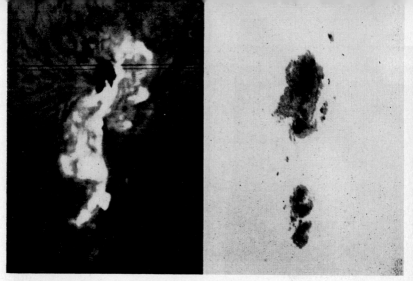

A hydrogen flare on the sun. The right photograph is in continuous light, while the left one is in hydrogen light. The bright flare on the sun can be seen in the left photograph.

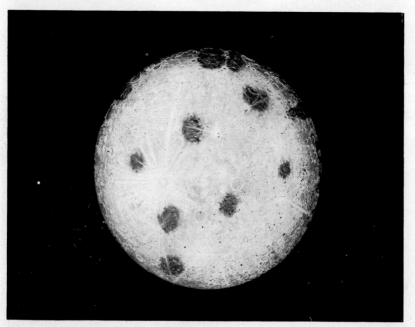

The other side of the moon? While we do not know what it is like, it is possible to draw a statistical picture of it. The number of craters and the smaller seas can be derived, but their precise position is a mystery.

The moon at the full phase. At this time, the rays or streaks can be seen to best advantage. The center of the ray system at the top of the moon is Tycho. Actually, it can be seen that one of the rays travels straight down and moves around to the other side of the moon. This ray leaves the moon at the bottom and a little to the left of center.

The Mare Imbrium region of the moon. Here the giant planetesimal hit to give rise to the seas on the surface of the moon. Towering peaks like Pico and Piton are visible in this area.

The south pole of the moon. At the third quarter phase the inordinately rough surface of the moon is seen to best advantage. The largest crater, Clavius—146 miles in diameter—is seen at the top of the photo and a little to the right of center. Tycho is the small round crater less than half way between Clavius and the bottom of the photo.

Portion of the moon containing the crater Alphonus. The suspected volcano is marked by the white arrow in the center.

falling in an elevator whose cables have broken, because both they and the vehicle will be traveling at the same speed, freely falling and weightless.

How will the passenger react to this giddy new sensation? Will he take it in his stride, can he become accustomed to it, or will he react so unfavorably that space travel will be forever impossible? Before we seriously plan trips to the moon or planets, these questions must be answered.

Many experimenters in various parts of the country have tried to find the answers. At the Randolph Air Force Base many subjects have been involved in flights which induce gravity-free conditions. Half became ill and the other half liked the new sensation. Dr. S. J. Gerathewohl of the School of Aviation Medicine conducted the experiments in which 46 men and one woman were involved in these so-called "baric" experiments. (The word "baric" is derived from the Greek *baros,* meaning weight.)

The vehicles used were a Lockheed T-33 and an F-94 jet. At an altitude between 17,000 and 23,000 feet, the pilot put the plane into a shallow dive, out of which he pulled smoothly so that the accelerations on the body did not exceed 1½ g's. The plane then went into an angle of climb of 60 degrees at full throttle, and then was pushed over into a dive. The pilot used the thrust or power of the engine to eliminate drag only, so the plane remained in a free-fall condition for the duration of the dive.

The results indicated that the reactions to free fall were highly individual. About half of the subjects felt comfortable during the period of weightlessness, even indicating that there was a pleasant feeling of slight elation during the experience. The other group reacted in two ways. One segment admitted to no emotional reaction, but confessed to slight forms of vertigo and nausea. The last segment, comprising about 30 per cent of all subjects, experienced discomfort, nausea, and other severe symptoms of motion sickness.

Practically all of the subjects reported sensations of floating or drifting slowly in free fall, pleasant to the first group. The second group rather vividly described sensations of tumbling, falling, rolling over, standing on their heads, or being suspended in midair in the inverted position. Attempts to prevent nausea were unsuccessful.

Several of the subjects reported sensations in motion and posture which differed from the actual conditions. They stated also that they were completely disoriented when they closed their eyes in flight. This experience is compatible with the concept that motion sickness is more often caused by the inability of the brain to handle incoming messages than by overstimulation. These sensory inconsistencies and conflicts lead to a breakdown with accompanying nausea.

This sensation is experienced on the earth's surface in the case of seasickness. On a boat, when the deck begins to meet the foot too soon, or to fall away from it, the conflicting messages arriving at the brain give rise to false impressions that make the subject seasick. In free fall, there is the same kind of disturbance. Here, too, conflicting messages are sent to the brain from various sources, the net result being a complete upset of the nervous system, the organ most sensitive to this type of shock.

One other discovery may be of great significance—that flying experience and conditioning prior to exposure to weightlessness affect the tolerance of the subject. Thus pilots of jet planes were found to be best suited to these conditions. And the fact that about half the subjects developed some tolerance to the conditions and actually enjoyed the experience leads the doctors to conclude that this problem, at least, can be resolved to make space flight a reality. However, they do urge caution in interpreting the findings so far on record. They point out that most people can stand 20 to 30 minutes of violent sea motion before the queasy feeling is triggered into seasickness, while the longest ride in free fall to date lasted only 60 seconds. Even 20 to 30 minutes in free fall may not be sufficient to provide the necessary answer. Some of the doctors suggest that a minimum of a 24-hour stay in gravity-free space is necessary before a definitive answer can be established. In that interval, a man would go through the routine of an entire day, eating his meals, monitoring his instruments, communicating with the earth, finally going to sleep and waking up—all in gravity-free space.

Orientation in space will be a problem. On the earth, in a gravity field, there are three senses which permit us to recognize where we are and in what position. The first is the visual sense which can tell us whether we are standing vertically and give us information concerning the behavior of objects around us. The second is the kinesthetic sense, which is gravity-oriented. The pull of gravity requires the tensing of certain muscles to hold us upright, and the awareness of this tension is the kinesthetic sense. The third is the vestibular sense which concerns the tiny organs in the inner ear containing the otoliths, or ear stones. This sense is also gravity-oriented. In gravity-free space, these latter two senses will be inactive. The question is, can we orient ourselves with only a single sense? Some experiments performed so far indicate that this may be possible.

But still another factor enters the problem when the vestibular sense cannot be used. A well known physiological law states that when a sense organ is not used, the sensitivity of the organ is at first increased. This can be illustrated as you sit in your living room at night; if all lights are turned off, your eyes eventually become dark-adapted, so that, if someone strikes a match, the light will appear very brilliant. In the same way, when the vestibular sense is not used, its sensitivity will increase. Under these conditions, if you turn your head slightly or nod it, conflicting stimuli will travel to the brain and their arrival may trigger a king-sized case of nausea.

Almost everyone has had falling nightmares; if you haven't so far, you will, because they are built into you. On earth, the recovery upon awakening is quick, as you feel the reassuring caress of the mattress on your body; soon you roll over and go back to sleep. Now, imagine that you are in a gravity-free condition, asleep and having a falling nightmare. You awake with a start, as on earth, but this time there is no reassuring caress of the mattress on your body. What do you feel then? Do you continue to have the sensation of falling? Can you rouse yourself and reassure yourself that you are not really falling but are instead in gravity-free space? The answers to these questions are unknown at this time and we won't know them until man gets into space. Restraint harnesses or well-tucked-in blankets may mitigate the confusion at least to some extent.

That living with this condition will be difficult is evidenced by experiments performed after Lt. Col. David G. Simons suffered severe disorientation and confusion upon waking from a nap during his balloon ascent in the Man-High Project. Because there was no ready explanation for this curious phenomenon, Dr. Harald J. von Beckh at the Holloman Air Force Base designed some experiments to deal with it, as well as with phenomena such as the effect of going rather quickly from high acceleration to weightlessness (as will occur when a man is put into an orbit) and from weightlessness to acceleration (as will occur in the re-entry from orbit).

An experienced pilot, with more than 600 jet flying hours, was chosen; he was indoctrinated in the experimental procedure and proper instruments were installed to give a complete record of his reactions. The trick was to get the man to fall asleep while riding in the plane, then waking him after the plane had gone into a gravity-free trajectory.

To get the subject to fall asleep he was kept awake for 48 hours, then fed a heavy breakfast so he would become drowsy. He boarded the plane and the pilot took him for a smooth ride, with no maneuver accelerations, until the subject fell asleep. Then the pilot put the plane into the proper Keplerian trajectory to achieve weightlessness; when that had been done, the pilot tugged on a string tied to the subject's arm and jarred him awake.

The subject was instantly in the highest state of confusion, feeling his arms and legs floating away and attempting to bring them back. He stated that he had never been so completely disoriented and confused in his life. Further experiments showed that if the subject experienced high accelerations followed by a weightless condition the disorientation lasted much longer. At 5 g's a subject would black out and at 6 g's he would lose consciousness, under normal conditions. But if the subject was first in free fall, then was accelerated, he blacked out at 3 g's and lost consciousness at 4 g's.

These experiments substantiated the findings of the Russians with the dog Laika in Sputnik II. The take-off accelerations resulted in a faster heart beat for Laika and, when she went into the weightless condition, the time required for the beat to return to normal was three or four times as long as it would have been if there had been no initial high accelerations.

Other experiments point up the difficulty of living in gravity-free space. Water from a glass "balls up," making it difficult to drink, because the only force on the water is surface tension. When squeeze bottles were used for drinking water, the subject knew what he was trying to do, but he had difficulty in aiming the bottle at his mouth. When the subject was requested to perform certain common coördination experiments, such as touching his forefingers together, touching his nose with a forefinger, etc., the performance at first was poor, but with practice there was some improvement.

Experiments of this kind can yield some knowledge of the behavior of a subject in gravity-free space; but until a human being is put into orbit around the earth, definitive answers will not be forthcoming. Being subjected to these psychological and physiological shocks will tax the nervous system of any man. It may be the inability of the average person to live with these conditions that will limit the number of people seeking to get into space.

CHAPTER 10

The Space Suit

The most scientific tailors the world has ever known are hard at work attempting to devise a suitable space suit. There is immediate need for one, because intrepid flyers riding the new X-series rocket planes on ballistic missile trajectories will encounter conditions very similar to those in space beyond the earth's atmosphere. The conditions are not too far different for altitudes of 20 miles or 20,000 miles, and a suit for either altitude must house and protect the human occupant.

Suits are available today and pilots are testing and using them. But these men will wear the suits for rather brief periods of time, and it is unlikely that our current models will resemble those necessary for men who will be working on the assembly of a space station a thousand or so miles above the earth's surface. The precise appearance of the final product is a matter of wide-open speculation; but we can be pretty sure that at first it will appear monstrous, grotesque, and altogether outlandish. A fantastic amount of research will have gone into its design and construction.

A space suit must outdo the old concept that a man's home is his castle. It must literally be his world—a world complete with an atmosphere to support human life, and with all manner of protective devices to guard man against the hazards to be encountered. In a way, we must think of a true space suit as a miniature space ship.

The primary consideration must be the provision for a breathable atmosphere inside the suit. Not only must it be provided, however; it must be retained securely, because the vacuum of space is an attractive place for molecules to escape into. The space suit, like the space ship, must be a hermetically sealed, escape-proof prison for air molecules. The suit must completely cover the individual, providing ample pressure so that the liquids in the tissues just below the skin do not vaporize, blowing up and destroying the tissue structure.

The pressure need not be the familiar 15 pounds per square inch that we enjoy at sea level on earth. Half of this or even less may do; but even this, unless a special fabric can be developed, will cause a flexible space suit to balloon out so that the occupant will be spread-eagled, and maneuvering or walking will be most difficult. Even with a space suit made of metal, with accordion-pleated jointed legs and arms, articulation of the arms, fingers, and legs may be very awkward. To obviate this difficulty, many space medicine doctors have advocated that the suit be a rigid capsule type of container—an overgrown can big enough to house the human and his protective devices, as well as the controls for the articulated manipulators extending from it. Very complex manipulators have been devised for performing exceedingly delicate operations in dangerous areas in our nuclear energy establishments, and it seems almost certain that something of this kind will be the solution of the space-suit problem.

While we may have solved the problem of manipulating tools and even, with a tractor-tread device, that of locomotion on the surface of a planet—surely anything resembling human legs would be foolish for this purpose—we have not begun to take care of the occupant of the can. The human body gives off heat, dangerous vapors, and water. We shall discuss the heat problem shortly, but just now we must think of the human body literally as a poison-generating machine. These waste products must somehow be removed, unless we can be sure that any individual's stay in the space suit will be of sufficiently short duration.

As has been noted, the pressure of the air in the suit may be even slightly lower than the $7\frac{1}{2}$ pounds per square inch under which certain Indians live and work high in the Andes Mountains. These natives have a higher lung capacity to make up for the shortage of oxygen at high altitudes; so, certainly, the air in a space suit must be enriched with oxygen. This might be only slight, however; weightlessness is a characteristic of space, and on the moon and Mars the surface gravity is much lower than on earth, and the occupant of the suit may be doing little more manual labor than the small task of pressing buttons with his fingers. But oxygen will be consumed, at the rate of slightly more than an ounce per hour, and carbon dioxide will be exhaled. A deep-sea diver expels from his suit "breathed" air as fresh air is pumped to him, but this will be too wasteful in space operations. Every ounce of air, either in a space ship or in a space suit, must be carefully preserved and rejuvenated for future use. An excess of carbon dioxide can be removed from the air in the suit by the use of suitable chemicals. There are several; sodium hydroxide is one such substance, sodium peroxide another, the latter not only absorbing the carbon dioxide but also returning the oxygen. We must not strive to remove all of the carbon dioxide, because this gas, by its sufficient presence in the air we breathe, produces the involuntary action of the diaphragm that keeps our lungs contracting and expanding. Some concentration of carbon dioxide well below the danger level of about 3% could pretty well be maintained.

One rather interesting aspect of the breathing problem in space is that we shall not have gravity to help us. It may be that we shall be forced to have a fan or other circulator in the space suit, to stir the air so we won't be breathing the same lungful over and over. This kind of forced circulation would also insure that the used air would be thoroughly mixed with the unused, and the mixture would pass over or through the purification chemicals.

The water given off by the human body would soon make the interior of the space suit a veritable Turkish bath unless it were taken care of. There are available today plastic suits that ladies wear while doing housework. These hold in the sweat so completely that the ladies literally stew in their own juices. The same discomfort from body heat and moisture is often experienced when one wears a non-porous plastic raincoat on a warm spring or summer day.

Water, too, can be removed from the air by chemicals or by circulating the air through cooling coils. There is need for some provision for at least mild refrigeration in the space suit, because the human body is a heat generator, also. Even lying quietly in bed, and even asleep, we generate heat— about as much as a 100-watt bulb. In a hermetically sealed can in the full glare of sunlight unattenuated by an atmosphere, the space man is going to be subject to a heat hazard.

The body must rid itself of the heat it is constantly generating. An increase of body temperature to 102° F. produces illness. With two more degrees, delirium sets in; a few more degrees bring about death. There is, then, an upper limit above which the body cannot go. Recent experiments indicate that the body can take external temperatures up to 140° F. How can this be reconciled with the figures given earlier? The answer lies in the ability of the body to lose heat through the evaporation of perspiration from the body. If the humidity is low enough, the external temperature can rise well above the danger point of maximum internal temperature. Unfortunately, the inside of the space suit will not normally be dry; the contained air will not only be hot but humid as well.

One suggestion has been that fresh oxygen be bled into the suit through a small orifice; the expansion in the jet action at the orifice, with consequent cooling, may absorb enough of the heat. But if we are to avoid using tanks of fresh oxygen, and instead rejuvenate the air, we shall have to rely on some sort of air conditioner. Just what form this will take is at the moment unknown, but before man undertakes to spend much time in space the solution must be at hand. Very recently, non-mechanical and rather

simple electrical means have been devised for lowering the temperature, and it seems certain that progress we can confidently expect in the next few years
will solve this problem.

There have been suggestions of capes as radiating
surfaces to be worn by the space men in the conventional comic-strip type of flexible suit. Perhaps suitable paint or other coating on the can-capsule suit
can control most of the direct solar radiation, but
we mustn't go too far with this. The vacuum of space
is a desirable goal not only for air molecules leaking
from the suit but also for the heat in the suit. It
may be simpler all around to make the capsule a
huge thermos bottle, with double walls.

There may be some cozy pairs of space men found
working around the skeleton of a space platform, or
exploring the moon. They will have the helmets of
their suits in contact with each other, in order to
communicate by sound. There is no air out there to
carry the sound waves, but sound could be transmitted from one space suit to another in contact
with it. Of course, reliance will probably be placed
on radio, but if there are a great many men at work
the empty vacuum may be criss-crossed and filled
with radio waves. Certainly each man must have his
own frequency of transmission and reception, or it
will sound like an intercom system in a great bomber
with every man of the crew talking at once. Even
with transistors and other advanced electronic com-

ponents, the weight and bulk of radio equipment may be deemed forbidding, but that is not likely. However, we must not lose sight of the fact that, while a little extra added equipment in each space capsule may not seem out of the question, all of this equipment must somehow be carried up into space in a rocket or a space ship, and the gross weight may be quite formidable.

The suit must protect its occupant from the blast of radiations from the sun and other objects in space. Any porthole must be of material that will absorb ultraviolet radiation, X-rays and gamma rays, for these are emitted from the sun in copious quantities. On earth, our atmosphere shields us from their lethal effects. The metal space suit, with appropriate material in the window, will serve the purpose, but cosmic radiation will not be diminished appreciably. As in a space ship, so in a space suit man must learn to live in an environment much richer in cosmic radiation, particularly the primary cosmic radiation consisting of high-energy particles whose effects we do not yet know.

There is no bright blue sky in space. Away from the sun, utter blackness spreads between the stars, and the stars themselves shine more brightly and unwaveringly because no air disturbs their beams. If the space suit turns so that the man who has been looking at the blackness of the sky suddenly sees the super-brilliant sun, his eyes may be seriously disturbed, if not damaged. There are no shades of gray in space, except perhaps inside the space ship or space suit where reflections or artificial illuminations are available.

As the space man can not always be sure that he will not look directly at the sun, we must make some provision for protecting his eyes. The author was involved in photo-electric photometry for some time and he believes that the photocell can furnish a solution to this acute problem. He can visualize a photocell mounted in the center of a pair of close-fitting goggles whose lenses consist of pairs of polaroid materials. A lens in front of the cell would direct light to it, so that it could look only straight ahead. The output of the cell, fed through an amplifier, could drive two tiny motors, or perhaps only one, geared to each side, to rotate the polaroids with respect to each other. Thus, if the illumination is high, the polaroids instantly become more nearly crossed, and less light enters the eyes. With low illumination, the photocell would sense that a change in the opposite direction is necessary, and the polaroids would uncross.

Perhaps an even simpler solution might be to provide no means for the occupant of the suit to look directly out of it. A complete television system could be provided, automatically adjusting itself to the intensity of the scene and providing a constant-brightness view on a screen before the space man's eyes.

Such systems are in existence today, weighing only a few pounds and quite adaptable to this purpose.

Getting around in space presents a considerable challenge. We have seen many illustrations of space men tied to the mother ship with nylon cords. This is all right if there are very few men and they need not drift too far away from the ship. Otherwise, there might be quite a tangled mess of nylon cords hampering the activities of the men. If the men are to work free, without any physical tie to the ship, they may drift rapidly away from orbit and be rescued with great difficulty.

Our space suits even more closely resemble miniature space ships when we realize that we must provide at least some of our suits with reaction motors. Only by ejecting a mass of matter in one direction can the space suit move in the opposite direction, in space. Small rockets or jets of some kind should be arranged around the center of gravity of the space suit, with very carefully-controlled degrees of strength. By judicious operation of one or more of these, the space man can then move his miniature world as he wishes. But the jets should be arranged and should be operated very carefully, else the space suit and its occupant will start to tumble end over end, with perhaps disastrous results.

We cannot know today what the space suit will look like or what it will contain for the comfort and protection of its occupant, as well as for its mechanical function in construction or exploration in space or on the surface of a planet; but we can be almost positive that it will in no wise resemble anything we have today or that we have seen in the familiar science fiction films, books, and magazines. We have a little time remaining, however, and perhaps we should not be too anxious to solve all of the problems instantly. After all, our robot satellites and probing rockets must tell us much more than we know today about this new environment, before we can proceed with full intelligence.

CHAPTER 11

Man on the Moon

During the night of August 7, 1958, there were reports that thousands of unaccustomed watchers of the sky were panicked by seeing what they believed to be a space ship approaching the moon. The object was the planet Mars, standing relatively motionless among the stars, not a space ship; and the moon, in its monthly trip around the earth, passed between us and the red planet. Mars was then almost 82 million miles from us; the moon's distance was almost 244,000 miles.

As these lines are written, the moon's distance is about 222,000 miles, and word has just been flashed that the Air Force moon probe "Pioneer," failing to achieve itst objective of going into orbit around the moon, has plunged back to earth in the South Pacific after having attained a maximum altitude of more than 79,000 miles. Launched at Cape Canaveral, Florida, at 4:42 A.M., E.D.S.T., October 11, 1958, the three-stage 52.2-ton, 88-foot-long rocket system reached its terminal speed of 23,500 miles per hour after only six minutes. But this speed was not quite enough, and the angle of injection was about 3½ degrees too high. Thus, after climbing for 27 hours, the instrumented probe started to fall back to earth.

Thus man's assault on the moon has begun. More and more probes are scheduled, and it is only a question of time before we orbit the moon, swing around it to return to the earth or impact on the moon. When man succeeds in this preliminary probe he will have achieved a goal of long standing, and his next steps will come into sharper focus.

Someday man will set foot on Mars and on Venus, but before that time he must walk on the moon. Indeed, he will use the moon as his point of departure for the other planets, establishing there a base for launching interplanetary rocket ships after assembling and fueling them there. But that may be at the turn of the century; whereas this writer believes confidently that around the year 1980 A.D. man will be established on the moon.

While this time scale is based on the expenditure of money at the $6 billion annual rate, there is a distinct likelihood that this scale may not be maintained—which, in turn, would invalidate the time tables. A spectacular break-through in the cold war in which binding treaties would be formulated with condign punishment for violators may drop the military spending precipitously, so that the rate of progress made in the past few years will not be continued. By the same token, the cold war suddenly becoming a hot war, with tremendous expenditure made for materiel for pursuing this war, will leave little for pure research in space travel. This too can set back the time scale for a significant period. Paradoxically, we appear to be living under the optimum conditions for research at this time.

A tremendous volume of preliminary work must be accomplished before man can occupy the moon. The most vital measure is the establishment of a manned space station—a huge earth satellite—as a base of operations. But there are some prior steps that can be taken, and the moon probes are among these.

One factor that recently has come to light urges us to guard against contaminating our satellite while landing anything on the moon. Biochemists and evolutionists are exceedingly anxious to know whether the germs of life on earth may not have come here through space, rather than originating here through the fortuitous combination of certain chemical elements in the distant past—perhaps several billion years ago. If organic molecules came to the earth from space, they may well also have landed on the moon, on Mars, and elsewhere. The life sciences experts would like to make sure that organic materials are not carried to the moon by our rockets except under conditions that will guarantee that we shall be able to determine if the moon has such molecules of its own. This is one of the aims of the newly-constituted Space Science Board of the National Academy of Sciences—National Research Council. With the possibility in mind that the device might crash on the moon, the Air Force Pioneer was thoroughly sterilized, both chemically and by radiation, before it was launched.

A visible marker on the moon could be placed there now; the payload of the Pioneer was 85 pounds, of which 25 pounds were instruments. It is almost certain that a slightly larger payload could be carried to create this marker.

The moon's surface is relatively dark—the average reflectivity is only about 7%—so a brilliant powder reflecting much more highly, if scattered over an area several hundred feet in diameter, should be detectable in large telescopes.

Then a small nuclear bomb could be detonated there. Several thousand tons of the materials of the lunar surface would be vaporized by the force of this explosion, and the flash would be easily visible to the naked eye. Through telescopes with spectroscopes attached to them, the light of the flash could be analyzed to reveal something of the composition of the lunar surface materials. While there is considerable sentiment against exploding an atomic bomb on the moon because of the resultant radioactive contamination, the results may warrant the use of this type of probe. We must possess concrete knowledge of the surface before a landing is attempted.

We believe today that the surface of the moon is dust—at least a fraction of an inch deep, and perhaps much deeper. That the surface is of loose material is evident from the way the moon's temperature changes between the time of high sun, when the temperature is above the boiling point of water, to a few hours after sunset, when it is 200° F. or more below zero. There is no detectable atmosphere on the moon—no water, hence no erosion in the ordinary terrestrial sense. However, particles do bombard the surface, in the form of meteorites and cosmic rays as well as atomic particles from the sun, to produce some pulverizing. Also, the severe changes in temperature can cause rocks to split, eventually to be broken to dust. This exfoliation, as it is called, is undoubtedly responsible for much of the dust we know to be there.

An atomic bomb set off on the moon would blast a much larger crater than the one the same bomb would produce on earth, because of the moon's lower surface gravity (only one-sixth as great as earth's). A rock weighing 1200 pounds on earth would weigh only 200 pounds on the moon; hence it would be lifted more easily and hurled farther, to produce with its fellows a new spot perhaps a mile or more in diameter. This would be easily visible from earth, especially if the sub-surface material were of a lighter color.

One stage in our conquest of the moon might be a double header, with instrumented satellites circling the moon relaying information back to us, and other instrumented satellites set down gently onto the moon's surface, to transmit data from there. Either one or both of these programs could easily come to pass very soon—certainly by 1965. To put a payload of 50 pounds of instruments and an equal weight of power supply on the moon will require retarding or braking rockets weighing about 550 pounds, so the total payload must be about 650 pounds. The rocket assembly to do this would weigh under a million pounds with the run-of-the-mill propellants available today. Exotic, high-energy propellants will reduce this all-up weight considerably.

The rocket system that launched Pioneer on October 11, 1958, consisted of three stages, the first being the standard Air Force Thor intermediate range ballistic missile weighing somewhat more than 50 tons with a thrust of 150,000 pounds. The second stage was a modified Vanguard weighing more than two tons, using liquid fuel delivering a thrust of about 7500 pounds. Here were also installed the eight spin rockets, to impart a stabilizing rotation of about 150 revolutions per minute to the third stage, an advanced Vanguard third-stage weighing more than 400 pounds, using solid fuel providing a thrust of 2500 pounds. This total weight included the 85-pound payload, the missile Pioneer itself, and the terminal solid-fuel rocket with a thrust of 300 pounds.

The 25-pound instrument package included devices to transmit information on the earth's and moon's magnetic fields, the frequency of micrometeorites (two impacts were noted), the intensity of radiations in space, and temperatures. It is believed that the terminal rocket failed to fire because the batteries to ignite it were too cold—down to about 36° F.

The details of moon probes are relatively unimportant, except for the fact that these Pioneers constituted the first. It can be expected that subsequent ones will become steadily more sophisticated until the time when we achieve a manned landing on the moon.

Despite its failure to orbit the moon, Pioneer has given us valuable information which would be enormously augmented if we could set an instrumented vehicle on the moon's surface to perform as a "lunar laboratory." The moon's gravity could be accurately measured, by instruments measuring how fast a known mass falls through a known distance, or how fast a pendulum of known length swings. The magnetic field of the moon and its changes, if any, could be determined. Measurements of the density of the atmosphere could be made, although we have been fairly certain for many years that this is far less than 1/10,000 of the density of our air.

Recently critical tests have been devised to detect an atmosphere. The most sensitive test involves the propagation properties of radio waves. The observation of distant radio sources occulted by the moon indicate that the atmosphere of the moon must be less than a ten-million millionth that of the earth. This is the equivalent of the density of the earth's atmosphere at 300 miles. There is a curious result of this. Meteors coming into the earth burn out beginning at altitudes of about 120 miles. Above this altitude there is insufficient atmosphere to create the friction to burn them out. Thus, if the moon's surface density is the equivalent of the earth's density at 300 miles, it can be said that no meteors can be seen to burn out on the moon.

A moon-circling device should be an instrumented vehicle weighing perhaps 400 to 800 pounds, containing photographic or television equipment or both, to examine the moon's surface more intimately than we can from the earth, and without the interference of our atmosphere. Particularly, we could thus get our first glimpse of the 41% of the moon's surface that we have never seen because the moon keeps about one hemisphere turned toward us; this will be discussed in some detail later in this chapter. The television images could be recorded on video tape in the vehicle, and sent to us on demand or at convenient times. With a precise guidance mechanism and additional rockets we might make the reconnaissance satellite come back to earth to deliver its findings to us.

An extension of this kind of vehicle could bring back to us actual physical samples of the materials of the moon's surface. This program involves the use of two moon rockets. The first rocket, designed to crash on the moon, would be armed with an atomic bomb. When the bomb explodes, an enormous amount of material will be tossed high above the surface—some of it, perhaps, even escaping the moon's gravitational field. Without a supporting atmosphere, finely-divided lunar material will fall quickly back to the surface; but, with exquisite timing, the second missile would swoop through the falling debris from the explosion and then would swing back to the earth by the use of auxiliary rockets provided for the purpose.

The problem of re-entry into the earth's atmosphere will by that time surely have been solved, so the capsule containing the sample of moon-dust can be safely landed here. With its arrival, and with the results from the "lunar observatory" and the moon-circling reconnaissance satellites at our disposal, it will be about time for us to send a manned vehicle to the moon—our first real step in the exploration of the remainder of the universe.

While these other programs are under way, the construction of a manned space station can be undertaken simultaneously. Revolving at a height of 1075 miles, the space platform will have an orbital speed of 4.35 miles per second. The velocity of escape from earth at this altitude is only 6.15 miles per second; hence we would need only about 1.8 miles per second additional to take off for anywhere in the solar system. The total performance required of a rocket in a space-station-to-moon round trip is much less than for a trip from the earth to the space station.

The ship that leaves the earth will most probably not be the one to go to the moon. In the first place, to get through our atmosphere a rocket must be streamlined. The ship that goes to the moon from the space station can have any shape at all, because there is no air resistance to be overcome. Because it is going to land on the moon, where gravitational attraction is only one-sixth as great as on earth, the ship can be constructed of much lighter materials, thus saving mass and reducing the power requirement. Of course, we must have the rocket jets for braking, to let the ship down gently on the moon's surface, and provision must be made for blasting off again for the return to earth.

It might be interesting to see just what the power requirements are. To leave the space station to get to the moon requires 1.8 miles per second; to land on the moon requires braking effort of 1.5 miles per second; to escape from the moon requires this same 1.5 miles per second, and to return to the space station and land there safely will require something like the same 1.8 miles per second that was required to escape. Here we have about 6.6 miles per second as our total power potential necessary for the round trip, in a straightforward shoot from the space station to the moon and return. However, if we establish ourselves in an orbit with the space station at a certain moment as its perigee and the moon as its apogee, we can use the earth's gravitational field to coast to the moon. Our power requirement would thereby be much reduced, although the time of travel would be longer.

However we go, it will probably not be before 1980, unless a major break-through in rocket technology occurs—either in the form of greatly improved chemical fuels and motors or some substitute such as nuclear-powered rockets, as outlined in Chapter 4. It should be easier from that time onward, however, because the chemical elements must exist on the moon as on the earth, and chemical fuels or working materials for the nuclear rocket motors could be manufactured on the moon and stored there for use on return trips. The fuel load to be taken from the earth to the space station and from the station to the moon will then be much reduced. It is conceivable, even, that a refueling satellite around the moon could be put in orbit, so space ships of the future could rendezvous with it to take on the fuel necessary for the gentle let-down on the moon, thus reducing still further the fuel load to be carried from the space station.

What will we find, and what will we do when we reach our satellite? First of all, we must combat all of the moon's gravitational pull with rockets, in the descent to the surface. There is no atmosphere there to assist our slowing down. Then, something that is at the moment an unknown factor must be squarely faced. We know that there is a layer of dust covering everything on the moon except perhaps the steepest slopes. To touch down in this dust may prove to be a hazardous operation. We have seen earlier that meteoritic infall and other processes have certainly produced a layer of dust, but estimates of its depth range from only a fraction of an inch to half a mile or more. Dr. Thomas Gold, now at Harvard University, believes that this layer may be quite solid at depths of several hundred feet, but "the top few feet," he says, "may well be extremely loose and more treacherous than quicksand."

"On the contrary," states Dr. Fred L. Whipple of Harvard University and the Smithsonian Astrophysical Observatory, "loose dust on the lunar surface is practically non-existent. The surface away from the immediate areas of large craters should have the structural strength of desert sand or possibly greater. . . . To the human (encased) foot or under vehicles the surface should be 'crunchy' and allow minimal imprint."

That it is important to decide—far in advance if possible—which of these two views is more nearly correct should be obvious. To land a rocket vehicle on the moon will require the use of retarding rockets. If these jets have something substantial to blow against as the ship settles down, a successful landing is more likely than would be the case if great volumes of dust were blown away by the jets and the ship were to settle into something like quicksand. An extreme catastrophe would be the toppling over of the ship, followed by the explosion of the fuel for the return trip. We may find that it is necessary to drop a high explosive on the moon's surface with the explosion directed in a horizontal plane, to clear away the loose dust down to a firmer footing.

Previous training at the space station will probably have accustomed the explorers to conditions of all degrees of gravity up to the earth's and beyond, so we must assume that they will be able to control their bodies under the lunar condition of only one-sixth of the earth's surface gravity. A 180-pound man on earth will weigh only 30 pounds on the moon, but his heavy and complicated space suit may well help him in this matter.

With no appreciable atmosphere on the moon, we must carry or manufacture our own. Water, too, must be supplied, at least on the early trips, and protection from the lethal radiations from the sun and from space. But we shall assume for the moment that these problems have been solved, and proceed to examine what the explorers will see and do on the moon.

If the landing is made in the middle of the full moon's face, the temperature of the surface may be as high at 275° F. A week later, as the sun sets for that place, the temperature will have fallen to about 100° F. below zero. And within a few hours, after the sun has actually set, the temperature is down to 200° F. below zero. The temperature continues to fall until at last the minimum of 240° F. below zero is reached just before the sun rises again, two weeks after it set.

These are the temperatures at the surface, as measured by radiometers attached to great telescopes. Below the surface, the temperature extremes are far less severe. Several inches down, as measured by radio waves that penetrate somewhat, the maximum is only about 80° F., the minimum about 110° F. below zero. And, of course, these are not the temperatures actually experienced by the moon explorers, because the practically non-existent atmosphere does not, as on the earth, carry the surface temperature to the surroundings. The sunward side of an explorer will be very hot, in the direct un-shielded glare, and the side away from the sun will be quite cold. To step from sunlight into shadow will mean a dangerous drop in temperature.

There is no bright sky on the moon, again because of the lack of atmosphere; with a shield for the eyes to protect them from the glare of the sun and the surface rocks, perhaps the brighter stars can be seen. If the sun itself is hidden behind a post or screen of some kind, the corona that from earth can be seen only at times of total eclipse will be easily visible.

The moon always keeps the same side toward the earth. It has done so for billions of years. Why?

Astronomers believe that a long time ago, when the moon may have been in a plastic state and much closer to the earth, the moon circled the earth a good bit faster. The tidal action of the earth on the moon pulled out enormous tides. When the moon solidi-fied the gravitational field of the earth captured this bulge, and the moon has been rotating once on its axis in the time it takes to circle the earth. While in the past the long axis of the moon was thought to be 7600 feet longer than the other two—recent rede-terminations have given the figure as 3600 feet. It is this difference which is enough to enable us to see the same side of the moon at all times, except for the small motions called librations.

The moon's axis is tipped a little with respect to the perpendicular to its orbit around the earth; so at one time of the month we see a little distance over the moon's north pole, half a month later we see the same distance beyond the moon's south pole. This is called libration in latitude.

The moon rotates at a constant rate, but because its orbit is an ellipse its motion around the earth is not constant; it travels fastest when it is closest to the earth, slowest when it is farthest from the earth. As a result we are able to see a little beyond the east limb at one time of the month and the same distance beyond the west limb half a month later. This is the libration in longitude.

In addition to these two librations just described, there is a small physical libration, as the moon rocks a little from side to side because the moon's figure is not exactly spherical.

The end result of these librations is that 41 per cent of the moon's surface is always turned toward the earth, 41 per cent is always turned away. And the remaining 18 per cent is alternately turned toward and away from us. So we have been able to see, from the earth, a total of only 59 per cent of the moon's surface. Somehow, the idea of 41 per cent of the surface never having been seen is very intriguing to the non-astronomer. To be sure, the astronomer would like to have a map of that hidden area of the moon, but he will be very surprised if there is to be

found there anything not represented in great pro-
fusion on the area that we are able to examine so
intimately today.

With no atmosphere to mellow the surface features, the moon appears very rough, and so it is, in
the large view. There has been no erosion there, in
the ordinary sense, because neither wind nor water
is available for cutting down the highlands and
filling up the lowlands. Even so, however, we can
easily recognize differences in age between many
groups of features, because there has been meteoritic
infall to pelt the older mountainous features, as well
as exfoliation that increased with time.

About 30,000 craters a mile or more in diameter
are known to exist on the moon, and it is estimated
that there must be at least several hundred thousand
more, smaller than that, on the visible surface. Some
of these craters are of tremendous size, up to 180
miles in diameter and two or more miles deep. Some
are so large that an explorer standing in the center
of one of them would not know he was in a crater,
because the sharp curvature of the moon's surface
would put the tops of the crater walls below the
horizon.

Large, dark, smoother areas, called "seas" by the
early observers, are dotted with small craters and
crossed by undulating low ridges. These areas were
perhaps produced by lava outpourings from great
sub-surface pools; the ridges may be the results of

moonquakes. While there must have been some igneous activity on the moon, similar to volcanism on earth, today most scientists believe that the lunar surface features for the most part were produced by the impact explosions of great meteorites. The earth has been struck by many of these; some of the craters are discoverable today, others eroded away with the passage of time and the scouring by glaciers.

The path of the moon is always concave toward the sun, so we may think of the earth-moon system as a pair of planets of unequal size, at the same distance from the sun, and close to each other. As they travel along they disturb each other, each moving around the center of gravity of the two, the barycenter, the point that travels their true orbit. Because of the greater mass of the earth, this center of gravity is inside the earth, only 3000 miles from the earth's center, and about 236,000 miles from the moon's center. Therefore, the moon appears to revolve around the earth and we speak of it as our satellite. More accurately, perhaps, we should call the moon our companion.

We know the moon's diameter—2160 miles—hence we know its volume. We know its mass—0.0123 that of the earth—so we can calculate the mean density of water; the earth's is 5.5 times that of water. If the moon did come from the earth, it came from the crustal mantle, because the density of 3.4 times water agrees very well with that of the surface materials of the earth. It is likely that the moon has no dense core like that of the earth.

We earlier glossed over the details of survival on the moon. Scientists believe the moon can support life from the earth. But after recognizing that air, food, and water, as well as equable climatic conditions, are necessary for life, and knowing that the moon has neither air nor water, how can we reconcile these statements?

In the next chapter we will discuss the details of a closed ecological cycle on the moon—how man will create a flourishing civilization on the moon.

CHAPTER 12

A Closed Ecological Cycle
on the Moon*

The concept of the moon being a cold, life-
less body perpetuated so many years by astronomers
will be relegated to the past when a manned landing
on the moon is consummated. This landing has been
tentatively set for the year 1980 A.D. Assuming that
this time scale is correct let us explore the feasibility
of establishing a self-supporting civilization on the
moon.

In the course of this analysis the principle assump-
tion made is that when the earth-moon system was
born the two planets had a common mother. To the

* This chapter represents the substance of a talk given by the author
to the Industrial College of the Armed Forces and the National War
College in Washington, D.C. on December 4, 1958.

author it is inconceivable that the composition of the moon can be too different from that of the earth. We will not discuss the controversial origin of the moon here; but no matter which thesis is favored, they all point to the fact that several billion years ago the earth-moon system came into being, and at that time they were so close that the compositions must be considered similar. With this premise let us explore the moon as a place where we can establish a self-supporting community.

The ability of the scientist to make the moon a veritable sink of materials for his welfare depends on the availability of energy in the future. The author firmly believes that in 1980 the thing we will have most of and which will cost least, except for taxes, will be energy. This will come from the fission of the heavy weight radioactive elements or from the fusion of the hydrogen atom. While the former is available today, and will increase in use in the immediate future, it is quite possible that the fusion of the hydrogen atom may not be realized for a generation or more. There is the further possibility that solar energy will be used. Bell Telephone engineers have developed silicon wafers tainted by some arsenic and boron which can transform the sun's radiation into electricity. This conversion has an efficiency of 11 per cent. These are indications that a breakthrough in this research field will be realized in the immediate future, in which the efficiency may reach

25 per cent. If we can bring this up to, say, 35 per cent, then our problems of energy generation are solved. From the sun may come the energy to help transform the moon from the bleak body we know today into a flourishing civilization.

On the moon the scientists can take the rocks, break them up, crush them, and then bake them to extract the water of crystallization from them. There is reason to believe that on the moon may be found magnesium silicates some of which contain 13 per cent water by weight. For every 100 pounds of rocks we can extract 13 pounds of water. Once this water has been extracted it can be electrolyzed, or even passed through tubes and subjected to ultraviolet radiations from the sun. The radiation will decompose the water into oxygen and hydrogen. Thus from the rocks on the moon will come an atmosphere, water, and hydrogen for fuel.

But this is only the beginning of a long list of materials which can be synthesized on the moon. To explore the wealth of materials which can be made, let us assume that in addition to the water in the rocks we also have available in the same rocks carbon, nitrogen, aluminum, calcium, iron, sodium, sulfur, potassium, phosphorus, and chlorine. We are going to assume that some of the rare noble metals needed for catalytic actions can be transported from the earth.

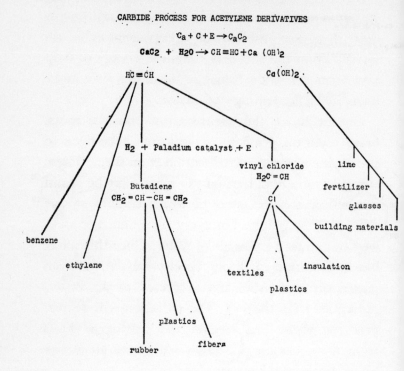

CARBIDE PROCESS FOR ACETYLENE DERIVATIVES

$$Ca + C + E \rightarrow CaC_2$$

$$CaC_2 + H_2O \rightarrow CH \equiv HC + Ca(OH)_2$$

HC ≡ CH

Ca(OH)$_2$

H$_2$ + Paladium catalyst + E

vinyl chloride
H$_2$C = CH

lime

fertilizer

Butadiene
CH$_2$ = CH − CH = CH$_2$

Cl

glasses

building materials

benzene

ethylene

textiles

plastics

insulation

plastics

rubber

fibers

The first process to be described* is the carbide process for acetylene derivatives. If carbon and calcium are combined and energy is necessary for this process we can get calcium carbide.

$$Ca + C + E \longrightarrow CaC_2$$

Calcium carbide plus water will give acetylene and calcium hydroxide.

* I am indebted to Ray Dalter, of the Franklin Institute Laboratories for Research and Development, for help in formulating these processes.

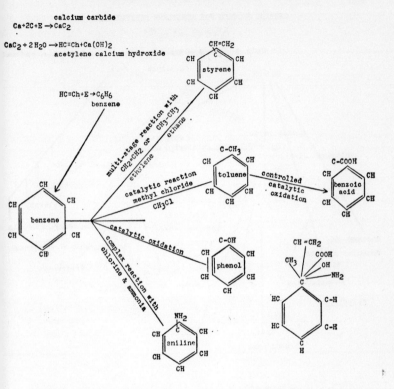

$$CaC_2 + H_2O \longrightarrow HC \equiv CH + Ca(OH)_2$$

Acetylene plus heat and a catalyst can be polymerized into benzene.

When benzene is subjected to catalytic oxidation we get the phenols; and these, in turn, give rise to medicinals, plastics, dyes, and intermediates for other chemical compounds.

Benzene can also give rise to toluene which in turn can give rise to benzoic acid. With the aid of catalysts

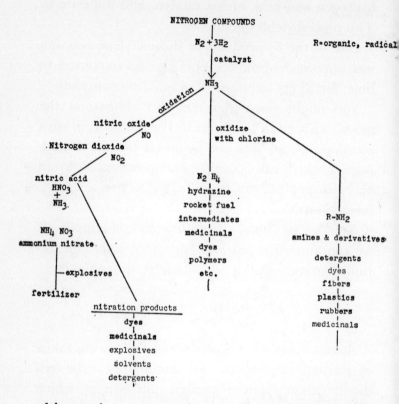

this goes into preservatives, medicinals, and food additives. It can also furnish the aromatic alcohols, esters, and building blocks for other compounds.

Toluene can also go to styrene, which gives us a whole family of plastics. If the styrene is reacted with butadiene plus a catalyst we get crude buna -S rubber. This can be built up with cross linkages and carbon to get stock for rubber products.

To get butadiene, we start with the acetylene, add

hydrogen and heat with a catalyst, and dimerize it. This process yields butadiene.

One of the by-products of the acetylene reaction was calcium hydroxide. This can be converted to lime, fertilizers, ceramics, and building materials.

You might want to make your clothes on the moon. This is not too difficult. We again begin with acetylene. From this can be made the vinyl compounds which can go to polymeric materials. From here we get plastics, textiles, protective coatings, insulation, etc.

Now let us explore the nitrogen compounds. If we combine nitrogen and hydrogen under the action of an iron catalyst, we can derive ammonia.

$$N_2 + 3H_2 \longrightarrow 2NH_3$$

Ammonia is the basic material for a wide range of synthesized products. The ammonia can be oxidized with a platinum catalyst plus oxygen, which gives us nitric oxide—NO. With the application of energy this goes to nitrogen dioxide NO_2. This with water gives us nitric acid. Now let's begin with this acid.

The combination of nitric acid and ammonia gives rise to ammonium nitrate, and this is the base of a whole group of explosives. Fertilizers can also be derived from this compound.

Nitration products like dyes, medicinals, solvents

and even detergents can be obtained from nitric acid.

If we begin with ammonia and oxidize it with chlorine we get hydrazine and other derivatives. From these come rocket fuels, dyes, polymers, and medicinals.

Finally, from ammonia can be acquired the amines and derivatives. These give rise to detergents, dyes, fibers, plastics, rubbers, and medicinals.

Now let's start with carbon monoxide and hydrogen. Using these two compounds and combining them with various catalysts like iron oxides, cobalt, molybdenum, etc., we can acquire a range of hydrocarbons. One of these is methanol CH_3OH, or methyl alcohol. When this is oxidized in the presence of a catalyst, we get formaldehyde HCHO. When it is combined with phenol, heat, and an alkali catalyst, we get the phenol formaldehydes, the bakelite series of plastic materials. These can be used for varnishes and for ion exchange resins.

From carbon monoxide and hydrogen we can also get methane. By heating this it can be broken down into ethylene C_2H_4, or the ethylene can be produced more directly by catalytic hydrogenation of acetylene. Ethylene can be catalysed into the polyethylene plastics. Ethylene can be hydrolysed with sulphuric acid and water to give ethyl alcohol which can be made into acetaldehyde which, in turn, can be oxidized to acetic acid. This is vinegar and a sol-

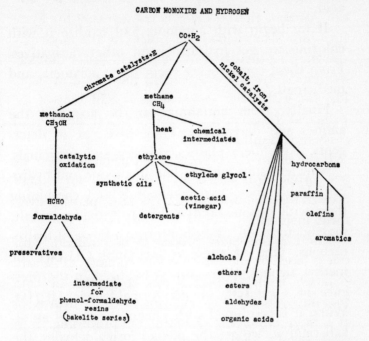

CARBON MONOXIDE AND HYDROGEN

CO+H₂

chromate catalysts+E

cobalt, iron, nickel catalysts

methane
CH₄

methanol
CH₃OH

heat   chemical
              intermediates

catalytic   ethylene
oxidation   hydrocarbons

              synthetic oils   ethylene glycol·

                                                paraffin
HCHO   acetic acid
                      (vinegar)   olefins
Formaldehyde   detergents
                                                aromatics

preservatives

                            alchols
                            ethers
          intermediate   esters
          for
          phenol-formaldehyde aldehydes
          resins
          (bakelite series)   organic acids

vent. The ethylene can also be oxidized to ethylene
oxide and, in turn, this can be reacted with substi-
tuted amine or ammonia to give detergents; or the
ethylene oxide can be made into methylene glycol
for anti-freeze compounds. The ethylene oxide with
the addition of the furfural alcohols can go to the
synthetic oils needed by an advanced civilization.

From the carbon monoxide and hydrogen comes
the long chain hydrocarbons which form the basis
for the paraffins, the olefins, and the aromatics.

Let's look at the sulphur compounds. We will assume there are iron pyrites on the moon. We also can postulate that nickel-iron fragments of the Mare Imbrium planetesimal are present on the moon. By just roasting these objects we can get sulfur dioxide. With a catalyst and oxygen this goes to sulfur trioxide, and with water we get sulfuric acid. One of the principal reagents for both chemical and metal processing is sulfuric acid.

If the sulfur is combined with carbon and heat we get carbon disulfide. This is the basis for rubber accelerators, flotation agents, thiourea, plastics, dyes, medicinals, etc.

There is one more process to be outlined. This one is based on sodium chloride—common table salt.

If salt is electrolysed it can be broken up into sodium hydroxide and chlorine. Sodium hydroxide is a most important chemical for processing. It is used in the manufacture of textiles, detergents, household cleaners, and in metal working. If it is combined with sulfuric acid to give sodium sulphate it again is used in textile processing, building materials, sulfate salts, fertilizers, etc.

Chlorine with a charcoal and iron oxide catalyst gives rise to hydrochloric acid, which is important in chemical and metal processing.

When reacted with hydrocarbons it gives rise to a wide range of important chemicals like trichlorethylene, methyl chloride, ethyl chloride, and vinylidene dichloride (saran). From these chemicals we

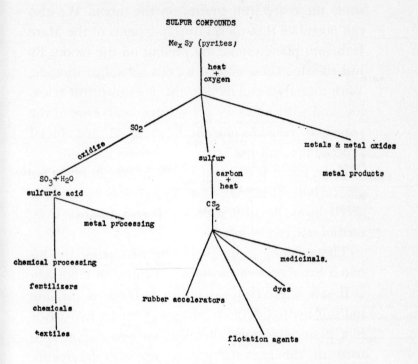

SULFUR COMPOUNDS

$Me_x Sy$ (pyrites)

heat + oxygen

SO_2

oxidize

metals & metal oxides

sulfur

metal products

$SO_3 + H_2O$
sulfuric acid

carbon + heat

CS_2

metal processing

chemical processing

medicinals.

fertilizers

dyes

rubber accelerators

chemicals

textiles

flotation agents

get detergents, rubbers, plastics, and medicinals.

When salt is reacted with ammonium bicarbonate we get sodium bicarbonate which is important in food and chemical processing. If the sodium bicarbonate is heated we get sodium carbonate, which is the basis of the glass industry.

Finally, purified salt is used in food, preservatives, and chemical processing.

These are but a skeletal few of the inordinately many chemical reactions in our technology. In all

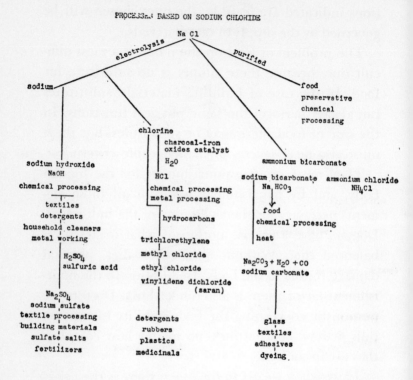

PROCESSES BASED ON SODIUM CHLORIDE

probability a chemist can fill a book of this size with reactions whose end products are vital to our economy. The purpose of this brief description is to show the technological patterns on which the scientist on the moon can call to support the community.

It should be remembered that the above reactions will be governed not by what is desirable but by what the economic situation dictates. We must realize that our economies on earth and on the moon will be completely different. While all of the reactions indicated are feasible, the ones chosen will be governed by the supply of raw materials.

The problem of food on the moon is a most difficult one, because there simply is no substitute for food. In the case of building materials, substitutes can always perform the same physical functions. In the case of food there may be substitutes, but these must also meet severe, unchallengeable criteria.

They must provide nourishment for the human body, and by nourishment is meant all those elements necessary for the well-being of the individual. Doctors have a precise notion of what makes up a balanced diet. Without a balanced diet, physical damage results to the body. In addition to the nourishment factor there is also one of bulk. Doctors are pessimistic concerning the body's ability to exist on pills or food concentrates, no matter how complete they are in content.

Thus, when we get to the moon there is the necessity of providing food for the traveler.

Extended research has been pursued in this field, and over the country many scientists are engaged in various facets of this program. For many years we have been hearing about the possibilities of growing a scumlike substance called algae, to furnish food and regenerate the atmosphere in a closed environment.

Photosynthesis is the key to the growth of algae. In this process this plant absorbs the carbon dioxide from the atmosphere; with mineral "spiked" water in the presence of light it will grow, increase in volume many times, and at the same time it will emit oxygen as a by-product of its metabolism. Thus, algae appear to be the ideal medium for providing food and the regeneration of the oxygen supply for space ships or enclosed areas on the moon.

However, a human being consumes about a ton and a half of food, oxygen, and water in a year. Except in rare cases the human being will not increase in weight to any appreciable extent. Thus the body wastes in the course of the year must precisely equal this ton and a half. What do we do with body wastes? We can't just discard them. In a closed or limited environment atoms are much too precious. Some mechanism must be designed to utilize these wastes. Algae provide an additional advantage for they can be used to process the waste material of the human organism.

Scientists call this a closed cycle and have indicated that in extended trips this will be a logistic necessity, because of the limitations of cargo space in any deep-space probe.

The idea of a closed cycle and the use of the same atoms over and over again is not pleasant to the average individual. However, it must be pointed out that we live in a closed cycle on the earth. The only difference between the earth and a space ship is the volume involved in the closed system. On the earth we have a great volume, and in the space ship or on the moon it is limited. Thus, in the space ship we would be more acutely aware of the closed cycle than we are on earth.

Of all the schemes advanced to furnish oxygen regeneration and food, the cultivation of algae appears to be the most promising. This plant grows best when agitated, when the proper nutrients are furnished, and when radiation of the proper wave length is available.

It has been estimated that to furnish enough algae to purify the air and to supply the food requirements necessitates a tank of about 50 square feet approximately 4 inches deep. Another way of expressing this is that we need 5 pounds of algae per day per man to keep him fed and breathing.

Because of the rapid turnover rate the five pounds is sufficient. Researchers point to the fact that it may be possible to increase the reproduction rate by a considerable margin. Under certain conditions there has been an increase in algae weight of from 7 to 8 times in a 24-hour day. However, recently a new type of algae has been discovered which will increase in weight over 1,000 times a day. This cuts the volume of the algae by a factor of about 20. If limited volumes can support a man in a closed environment, then this can be looked upon as a major breakthrough in our attempts to colonize the moon.

Chlorella Algae are composed of 50 per cent protein, 15 per cent carbohydrate, 25 per cent liquids, and about 10 per cent ash. The makeup varies with the nutrient solution. If the solution is a thin suspension the proteins may increase to 70 per cent or more. Proteins react favorably to blue light in the illumination. One of the most important elements in the culture is nitrogen. A dropping off of the nitrogen content may decrease the protein content to 15 per cent. What we get as food is highly dependent on the concentration of nitrogen used.

In addition to the nitrates, trace elements are essential to the plants. Elements like cobalt, manganese, copper, phosphorus, etc., are essential to the proper metabolism of the body. The trace elements must be added in precise amounts. An excess of some minerals can be toxic to the plant or deleterious to the human being. If difficulty is found in keeping some of the minerals in solution then, chelating agents must be used.

Thus, even with what appears to be simple plant life great care must be taken, to insure that the product will sustain the space man.

It should be realized that once the green scum has been collected we cannot go directly to, say, algaeburgers, and eat them. Many steps are required to go from scum to food. But scientists are aware of them and feel certain that they can make the transitions though certain difficulties have recently become evident.

Dr. Syrrel S. Wilks, of the School of Aviation Medicine at Randolph Field, has found that under certain conditions, when the algae suffer damage, they may not give off the highly desirable oxygen as a metabolic by-product. Instead they may give off the lethal carbon monoxide which, it must be admitted, won't do the space traveler a bit of good. Close study of this problem is required before algae can be considered the ideal mechanism to provide food on the moon.

Some studies have indicated that the algae seem to lose their ability to reproduce with age. If this proves to be true it would deal an almost fatal blow to the schemes which use this for food and atmosphere. There are, however, indications that introducing spores from algae "stores" will apparently rejuvenate the entire culture. The work being done in this field must achieve definitive answers before man can relie on the algae for food.

A successful settlement on the moon may, in time, also require hydroponics. This science is about 50 years old but only recently have significant advances been made in it. It can be shown that it is an efficient growing system, for in this method the chemicals needed by the plants are always available; the chemicals and the nutrients are in solution, and the roots of the plants are in intimate contact with the solution. Hydroponics may evolve as a most simple system.

In this science, plants can be grown from seeds with an extraordinarily high yield. Germination of the seeds is virtually 100 per cent, and in the transplanting the seedlings grow without interruption. In addition to the high yield there is also the added advantage that there are no soil pests or disease to harm or kill the plants or cut the yield.

At this time hydroponics merits serious study as a source of food on a place like the moon. All that we need—the minerals or chemicals, carbon dioxide and radiation—will, we believe, be present in unlimited supply on the moon. Once we get to the moon it is likely that the closed cycle can be maintained and the space men can live "off" the moon.

The ability to create as outlined in this chapter is not the only criterion for establishing a civilization on the moon. There will come a time in the not too distant future when the moon as observed from the earth will be completely different from the way we see it in tonight's sky. At that time, when we see the full moon, we may see it peppered with tiny brilliant points like the reflection from a diamond. These reflections will come from the plastic shells which house the settlers on the moon. These will remake the surface of the moon in much the same manner as man has remodeled the surface of the earth.

It is highly unlikely that the early settlers on the moon will be the pure scientists—the physicists or the astronomers. These represent the most unlikely people to send on the first trips to the moon. The colonizers of the moon can be likened to the early explorers who came to this country. These explorers had one thing in common though their backgrounds were varied—they were builders. Even the preacher who catered to the spiritual needs of the community was a hardy individual who could build his own house and provide food for himself and his family. Likewise, those who go to the moon first will be the all-around technicians, craftsmen, engineers, and communications experts. These are the people who will lay the groundwork for those who follow.

CHAPTER 13

Navigation and Travel to the Planets

When man gets off the earth into space, one of his most pressing problems will be to know where he is and to find out just how to get to where he is going. Navigation in space will be one of the most complex procedures with which he will have to cope. Even the slightest miscalculation in position or direction may doom an entire space expedition. To get some idea of the problem, let's examine some of the procedures used on earth.

The terrestrial navigation problem is relatively easy because we have everywhere a well-established standard of a vertical line and a horizontal plane, determined by the pull of gravity. We know at every moment just what point on the earth is exactly under a particular star that we may observe. We can meas-

ure the altitude of the star above the horizon and
subtract this from 90 degrees, to get the star's distance from our zenith, and this is the angular distance
from our position to the place exactly under that
star. The direction of the star tells us the direction
in which that sub-stellar point lies. We thus locate
our position and, by considering it and our desired
destination, we can tell which way to go to achieve
our goal.

Except when we might wish to rendezvous with
another ship at sea, our goals are fixed and we can
know that, if we head in the proper direction for a
certain length of time, we must get there. We may
choose any one of many paths, depending on our
degree of impatience or other considerations. In
space, our targets are all moving, and we are constantly harried by the fuel problem and others involving physical considerations such as food supply
and air purification, as well as possible psychological
problems such as the tedium of long voyages in
space.

In space, new navigational problems are encountered. Our fundamental plane of the horizon
no longer exists, because there are only the atten-
uated gravitational pulls of many bodies, and not
the strong pull of one. Even if the body is a satellite
circling the earth, it is endowed with centrifugal
force that neatly balances the gravitational field of
the earth. But, once the orbit of the satellite is

established, various types of devices exist or are in development to indicate at all times the direction away from the center of the earth. Of course, in orbit around the earth, it is really unnecessary to do any navigating; but out in space, on a journey to another planet, we must have some means of knowing if we are on the right course.

Some fundamental direction should be established in space, and one solution is to keep the space ship so oriented that the long axis of the ship always passes through the sun. Only in an atmosphere is streamlining necessary; out in space a ship may travel sidewise as well as lengthwise, because there is no appreciable friction. Telescopic sights of great accuracy could be provided, to establish this fundamental line to the sun. Once accomplished, suitable side jets or other devices could maintain this line and give us the first requirement of a navigational system.

Away from the earth and its daily rotation, the stars are truly fixed, changing their positions only as the space ship changes its orientation. We can then measure our ship's longitude and latitude, referred to a new frame of reference. The fundamental plane in this new frame of reference is the ecliptic, the plane of the earth's orbit around the sun. Longitude will be the angle between the line joining us and the sun and some fundamental line arbitrarily chosen for the purpose. It might be the line joining the sun with some star or, probably, some point referred to several stars, inasmuch as it is unlikely that a suitable star will be found exactly on the ecliptic. The latitude of the ship would be the angle between the line joining the ship and the sun and the plane of the ecliptic. This space latitude and longitude could be determined by observations of the stars.

Another solution to the problem of position in space comes from Dr. Roy d'E. Atkinson of the Royal Observatory of England. He suggests that simultaneous observations of two or more planets with respect to the background of the stars will locate the ship at the point of intersection of lines of sight, much as a coastwise shipping lane can be picked out by observations of two or more lighthouses or other landmarks, in the kind of terrestrial navigation known as piloting. A small computer aboard the space ship might make possible fast solutions to navigation problems, or the information could be radioed back to earth to have the computing job done, and the results radioed back to the ship. This process of doing this calculating on earth would have the advantage that, as soon as the exact time of blast-off and the initial path were known from observations on earth, tables for location of the planets could be quickly computed for the entire trip, and radioed to the ship en route.

In Chapter 2 we found that from our moving

earth, whose motions are well known, we can make three or more observations of another moving body and determine its path and position in space. In space, we can simply reverse this process by making observations of a planet or more planets with respect to the star background and use our knowledge of the positions and motions to determine our own positions and motion. Again, the calculations need not be made on the ship; the observational material might be radioed to computers on earth for the solutions.

Dr. Atkinson suggests that, inasmuch as many trips—especially to the moon and to other planets—will lie very close to the plane of the ecliptic, we can use several suitable stars near the ecliptic to find our longitude. There are four of them brighter than the North Star within a belt 10 degrees wide, centered on the ecliptic, and they are distributed almost uniformly around the ecliptic. It should be possible on many trips to simplify the problem considerably by choosing a star with a longitude close to 90 degrees from the direction of motion.

For latitude determinations, a star close to the pole of the ecliptic is chosen. Canopus, a brilliant star in the southern hemisphere, is reasonably close to the south ecliptic pole. Dr. Atkinson points out further that, if we can be sure of identifying somewhat fainter stars, then one in Draco, the Dragon, about a third as bright as the ecliptic stars, is the one to use for the north ecliptic pole, because it is less than one degree distant from it.

One factor in our astro-navigation has been omitted so far. On earth, we have two angular measurements of location—latitude and longitude; but we have no great problem with one factor—our distance from the center of the earth. Even in airplanes we are essentially still on the earth's surface. Out in space, if we are using the sun as the origin of longitude and latitude coordinates instead of the center of the earth, we must establish our distance from the sun. Even when we determine our position and orbit by observing the planets, and we can determine our position within 5,000 miles with respect to the sun, it would be convenient to have a check on our observations.

We can measure the sun's angular diameter which, as seen from the earth's mean distance from the sun, is about 1918 seconds of arc. If we measure the angular diameter carefully, anywhere in the solar system, we can determine the sun's distance. At the orbit of Mars, by conventional methods we might achieve an accuracy of measurement of about one part in three or four thousand, corresponding to a distance error of about 40,000 miles. But recent developments indicate that even greater accuracy can be available.

The Radio Corporation of America Laboratories have developed a novel photocell, of the new semiconductor junction type. Pointed at the sun, with a collimating lens feeding it with light, the variation of light intensity from one edge of the sun to the other can be detected. An accuracy of about a tenth of a second of arc is looked for—one part in about 20,000 at the earth's distance from the sun—good enough for space navigational purpose. The Mars trip could be accomplished with an error of only about 7,000 miles, instead of the 40,000 miles that were mentioned earlier.

With our angular position determined from star observations and the linear measurement of the distance of the sun, or from observations of the positions of planets or other objects, we can pretty well know where we are in space. But, of course, we must make sure that we have set off in such a way that our path is one that efficiently uses our potentialities of fuel, storage space for food, and every other aspect of space travel.

Our paths to the planets and the time intervals required will be governed by the type of fuel available. If fuel were no problem, we could set off into space and chase any planet we might choose, wasting fuel because of lack of forethought. But this is hardly an intelligent approach to the problem that is going to involve so much preparation and money.

In 1925, Dr. Walter Hohmann, a German space-flight pioneer, published his analyses of the mechanics of spaceflight paths, in which he emphasized the importance of those that were tangent to the planetary orbits. Without a major break-through in the fuel problem, these orbits are the only ones that make sense. Dr. Hohmann pointed out that these are the most economical paths because we take advantage of the sun's gravitational field. Once we have shaken loose from the earth, our path to another planet should be an orbit around the sun— an ellipse with the sun in one focus. Our initial take-off from an orbiting space platform, or from the moon, would be directed toward letting the sun's gravitational field provide the motive power to get our space ship to its destination. The shape and other characteristics of such an orbit are easy to define and we can know in advance, within narrow limits, the fuel and the other requirements for the trip.

Unfortunately, these Hohmann orbits require considerable time. In the neighborhood of the earth, one orbital trip will require a year; at the distance of Mars, the time is almost two years.

The planets closest to the sun move most rapidly. Mercury travels in its 88-day orbit with a speed of 29.8 miles per second, compared to the 18.5 miles per second for the earth and 15.0 miles per second for Mars. Venus and Mars will probably be the first planets visited by space ships from earth. The minimum distance from earth to Venus is about 26,000,000 miles, but to use an economical path to this planet we must travel about 250,000,000 miles. To

Mars, at nearest approach, the distance is about 35,000,000 miles, but our trajectory to the planet will be about 345,000,000 miles.

Let's first consider the trip to Mars. We shall assume that we are using the moon for a space platform. The problem is to fight the sun's gravitational pull and move out beyond the earth's orbit toward that of Mars. If the take-off time and the direction of travel are just right, the trip will require about 258 earth days. The path will take us halfway around the sun and finally Mars will overtake the space ship. The landing will probably be made on one of the Martian satellites, and from there ferry ships assembled from the materials of the space ships can carry us to the surface.

One factor that is seldom considered is that we can't arbitrarily choose, at least in the early days of space travel, the moment of departure on the return trip. The most efficient path is going to be one that is predetermined and we must wait for the conditions to be just right. There must be a waiting or "stop-over" time on the planet, to permit the earth and Mars to arrange themselves for a proper rendezvous.

This waiting time on Mars is 455 earth days. Then the space ship can leave Mars (or one of its satellites), lose some speed to permit the sun's gravitational field to take over, then go without power to the earth's orbit. The ship will get there first, and then the earth will overtake it for an easy landing. This return will require 258 days, as did the outward trip, thus making the total time for a round trip to Mars 971 days—about two years and eight months.

In a round-trip to Venus, our speeds are higher because we are going closer to the sun; therefore, the trip will take less time. The trajectory to Venus requires only 145 days, and so does the return trip; but, curiously, the stop-over period is longer for Venus than for Mars—470 days. This gives us a total of 762 days for the round trip—about two years and one month.

Strangely, we could get to Mercury and back in only 277 days—only 19 days longer than the trip one way to Mars, despite the fact that we are, at our nearest approach, about 56,000,000 miles from that innermost planet. If our time is really limited and we don't mind very inhospitable conditions when we get there, Mercury is the planet to visit. Only 105 days are required for the trip to Mercury, and the same time for the return; but the layover time, because Mercury moves so quickly, is only 67 days.

The planets Mercury, Venus, and Mars are the only ones convenient to reach. Next is Jupiter—and that's a trip really to reckon with. This planet is about five times as far from the sun as the earth is, so the trip is long. Transit time is 997 days, almost two years and nine months. The layover time is 213 days, and the return trip requires another 997 days.

A total of 2207 days, then, is required for the round trip—a few days over six years.

To go to Saturn and return will take us about 12 years; for Uranus the round trip will require about 30 years. To either Neptune or Pluto, the round trip requires about 61 years. These two planets can be considered together because Pluto's orbit at perihelion is closer to the sun than the average distance of Neptune.

From these figures it is easy to see that to explore the outer reaches of the solar system will mean leaving the earth for a major portion of one's lifetime; in the case of the two outer planets, a 19-year-old youngster leaving the earth would return an old man of 80—not a very attractive prospect.

However, it may well be that technological advances may make possible travel to these outer planets in other than economical orbits. If an unlimited source of power were available, then instead of elliptical orbits we might be able to use high-speed hyperbolic paths.

If at some time in the future, as we shall discuss in Chapter 14, we can find the power to speed us along the way at, say, 30 miles per second instead of the six or seven miles per second available with chemical fuels, then the transit time for the Mars trip would be cut down from 258 days to 44 days, and for Pluto from 10,972 days to 1,916 days.

Now, while we are speculating, let's assume that at some distant time in the future a speed of 100 miles per second will be available. Then the trip to Mars will be cut to 10 days and that to Pluto to 330 days. With this speed, exploration of the solar system would become as easy, time-wise, as exploration trips on earth today.

CHAPTER 14

Our Nearest Neighbors: the Planets

After the conquest of the moon, man will surely set his sights on other planets of the solar system. The excitement of exploration has always quickened man's blood and given succeeding generations something to shoot at, beyond what has gone before.

Suppose we take a look at possible destinations, not in the order in which they will be attempted, but in the straightforward order of distance from the sun. The innermost known planet is Mercury, the smallest of the major planets, with a diameter of 3,100 miles, although recent studies indicate that it may be only 3,010 miles. Its mass is difficult to determine, except as it can be found to disturb other bodies, but recent determinations from Mercury's per-

turbations of the motion of Venus give a value of
0.053 of that of the earth. Inasmuch as its volume is
close to 0.055 that of the earth, its density comes out
at about 5.3 times that of water, second only to the
earth's of 5.52 times water. Its surface gravity is only
0.37 that of earth, and the velocity of escape from
its surface is 2.6 miles per second.

At a distance of only 36 millions of miles from the
sun, this planet hurries once around in a period of
only 88 days and, probably because the sun has
produced a tidal distortion of its figure, we find that
its rotation period on its axis is also 88 days. Mercury,
then, keeps one face in general turned always toward the sun, as the moon keeps one face to the
earth. Again, as with the moon, there are librations
to put a fringe area alternately in sunlight and in
darkness. Mercury's orbit is a rather eccentric ellipse;
the mean velocity is nearly 30 miles per second.

Because of Mercury's proximity to the sun, the
surface temperature on the illuminated hemisphere
is very high; in the center of that face it is above
700° F., hot enough to melt lead. The side away
from the sun is exposed to the bitter cold of space.
Because of Mercury's low surface gravity and the
high temperature of one side, it is theoretically
impossible for it to have any but the most momentary
and scanty atmosphere, somewhat like the moon.
There are faint markings on its surface, difficult to
see, and we know very little about this planet.

Next outward from the sun is Venus, at a mean distance of 67.2 millions of miles. Its orbital period is 224.7 days; the planet travels its most nearly circular of all planetary orbits at the average speed of about 22 miles per second.

The mass of Venus is 0.815 that of the earth and the diameter is 7,700 miles, so the mean density is 4.95 times water. The surface gravity is 0.86 that of the earth; the escape velocity is 6.4 miles per second.

How much of the apparent diameter of Venus is atmosphere we do not know, because the dense gaseous mantle of this planet precludes our seeing its surface. The spectroscope discloses that in this atmosphere carbon dioxide is present in abundance. The telescope disclosed dusky bands in the atmosphere, probably at the highest levels. There are from three to seven present and these Dr. Gerard P. Kuiper used in 1954 to determine that the equator of Venus is inclined at an angle of 32 degrees to the planet's orbit. Kuiper concluded that the rotation period is a few weeks. Dr. R. S. Richardson, of the Mt. Wilson and Palomar Observatories, from his 1956 observations concurs with Kuiper. However, Dr. A. Dollfus at Pic du Midi, as recently as 1955, put the period at 225 days—identical with the period of revolution around the sun. In 1957, brief bursts of radio noise, perhaps akin to lightning flashes on earth, were discovered, and from them Dr. John D. Kraus of Ohio State University announced a period of rotation of 22 hours 17 minutes, with an uncertainty of 10 minutes. Recent astronomical meetings where this was discussed indicate that workers in the field are critical of the radio results. At the moment we must consider the rotation period uncertain.

No trace of oxygen has been found in the atmosphere, but N. A. Kozyrev, at the Crimean Observatory, thought in 1955 that he detected the auroral bands of ionized molecular nitrogen there, as well as some other auroral indications of unidentified materials. He gave the temperature of the outer atmosphere of Venus as almost 200° F. below zero; he estimated the surface temperature of the planet as about 85° F. above zero.*

Much of the atmosphere may be occupied by dust swept up from the surface of the planet by ferocious winds born of the planet's proximity to the sun. There has been one line of theoretical speculation suggesting that water may lie on the surface of the planet and that it may not be too hot there (confirming Kozyrev's conclusions), the carbon dioxide acting as a screen to prevent too much surface sunlight.**

The third planet from the sun is our earth, and its physical characteristics are fairly well known to us, as outlined in Chapter 1. The distance from the

* However, until such time as these temperature estimates are confirmed their reliability is suspect.

** Recent observational evidence seems to contradict the Whipple-Menzel theory that the clouds are water. Venus at this time is really the planet of mystery and will certainly be an attractive target for future space travel.

sun is 93 millions of miles, the period of revolution is what we call a year, the period of axial rotation is what we call the day. Earth is the first planet we encounter that has a satellite; Mercury and Venus travel alone around the sun.

Beyond the earth lies Mars, at a distance of 141.5 millions of miles from the sun. The orbit of Mars is more eccentric than earth's, so as the earth catches up with Mars and passes it approximately every two years, sometimes the distance is much less than at other times. The closest approaches of the two planets—the very shortest being 34.6 millions of miles—occur at intervals of either 15 or 17 years. The latest was in 1956, the next will be in 1971.

This red planet revolves around the sun with an average speed of 15 miles per second in a period of 687 days and, from the surface markings observed over long intervals of time, the rotation period is quite accurately determined as 24 hours 37 minutes 22.67 seconds. The diameter of Mars is 4220 miles, its mass is accurately known from the motions of its two satellites as 0.107 that of the earth, and its mean density works out as only 3.95 times water—only little more than the density of the moon or of the surface rocks of earth. The surface gravity is 0.38 that of the earth. The escape velocity is 3.1 miles per second, which means that it should be fairly easy to set a space ship down on its surface and, later, to take off again.

Because of the low surface gravity, Mars cannot hold a very dense atmosphere, although its distance from the sun, producing a range of temperature from about 80° F. above to about 100° F. below zero, means that the molecules travel more slowly and hence do not escape quite as quickly as, say, from Mercury. That the planet has an atmosphere is beyond doubt. The surface features are sometimes veiled by clouds of at least three kinds. There are white clouds at high levels, perhaps five to fifteen miles above the surface, and these seem to be made of ice crystals, like the cirrus clouds of earth; yellow clouds, probably of dust swept up by moderate winds, lie at levels below five miles. Still higher than the white clouds are blue ones, usually in the sunrise or sunset regions of the planet. The atmospheric pressure at the surface of Mars is of the order of only three or four inches of mercury as compared with 30 inches for the earth—about that at an altitude of 11 or 12 miles here.

In 1947, Kuiper discovered carbon dioxide in the atmosphere of Mars, about twice as much as we have here; because of the lower surface area of Mars, there must be about seven times as much over each square mile of that planet as we have on earth. Oxygen is not found in the Martian atmosphere, but water vapor there is attested to by several lines of evidence. For example, there are polar caps to the planet that wax and wane with the seasons, and both

Kuiper and Dollfus have demonstrated that sublimation (the passing directly from ice to water vapor) is going on in the atmosphere just above the caps. But the snow and ice of the caps form a layer probably less than an inch deep, and contain less water than do our Great Lakes. Dr. S. L. Hess of the University of Florida has calculated that, free in the atmosphere of Mars, there can be no more water than would make a layer 0.00008 inch deep, if it were all on the surface of the planet. If we were to collect all of this water into a lake or pond, just one foot deep, it would cover a circle 21.5 miles in diameter; this is about three-tenths of the area of Rhode Island. In 1956, Dr. C. C. Kiess of the National Bureau of Standards—National Geographic Society set up a powerful spectroscopic observatory on Mauna Loa, at an altitude of 11,134 feet, above most of the confusing materials in the earth's atmosphere. His observations showed that the layer of water on Mars, if all of it were precipitated, would be less than 0.003 inch deep. This would make a lake one foot deep with a diameter of 136 miles, having the combined area of Massachusetts, Rhode Island, and Connecticut.

It is very likely that nitrogen and argon, as well as other materials, exist in the Martian atmosphere, but these cannot be detected spectroscopically. Dr. A. de Vaucouleurs has suggested as the possible composition of that atmosphere the following: Nitrogen

98.5%, argon 1.2%, carbon dioxide 0.25%, oxygen, water, and other materials 0.05%. We might compare this with earth's nitrogen 78%, oxygen 21%, argon, carbon dioxide, and other materials 1%.

Certainly we won't be able to sustain life by breathing this thin Martian atmosphere, but it will serve to minimize meteoritic bombardment and probably will eliminate the need for a complete space suit. Also, space ships will be assisted in landing by the aerodynamic braking possibilities.

There are many who believe that a low form of plant life is present on Mars. Dr. William Sinton, of Harvard College Observatory, has discovered a feature in the infrared spectrum of an absorption feature near the wavelength of resonance of the CH bond which implies the existance of organic molecules on the planet.

If we speculate on the significance of this feature we come up with some intriguing conclusions. The presence of organic molecules and the seasonal changes on the planet's surface lead to the conclusion that a low form of plant life—like the mosses or lichens—may be present. And if these are present it may also be necessary to postulate the existence of some form of animal life to oxidize the plant life.*

While the answers to these questions are unavailable today, in the immediate future when the "bal-

* For a description of the type of animal life that could exist on Mars, see *A Space Traveler's Guide to Mars,* by the author, published by Henry Holt and Co., 1956.

loon observatories" become highly efficient or when an observatory in space is established we will be able to check the surface detail to draw conclusions as to what is present there. The resolving of the surface conditions of Mars is one of the most challenging problems of the space age.

A vast structure of surface detail is visible on Mars, drawn by many observers as thin, straight lines to which the name "canals" unfortunately was given. Other observers, using fine telescopes in more favorable observing sites, see these lines as mottled, blotchy streaks, not at all continuous and much more likely to be natural features. In addition to these lines, there are the greenish areas already mentioned, but most of the surface of Mars is of a reddish ochre color, giving the planet the hue we see with the unaided eye. Some have suggested that in this lies the reason for the scarcity of atmospheric oxygen on Mars; the reddish color may be due to pulverized oxides of iron, such as the mineral limonite on earth. Perhaps it is due to a silicate of aluminum and potassium called felsite; this is an igneous rock. Whatever the reddish areas consist of, we can be pretty sure that they are the wastelands, the deserts, of a planet that, for all practical purposes, we must count as almost totally a desert as compared with our watery, green earth.

Mars has two satellites. Phobos is only about 3,700 miles from the surface of the planet; the period of revolution is only 7 hours 38 minutes, so that it appears to rise in the west and set in the east, on Mars, three times a day. Phobos has a diameter of no more than 10 miles; from Mars it would appear about one-sixtieth as bright as our moon does to us, but it would seem only one-third as wide. The other satellite, Deimos, only about 5 miles in diameter, would appear to be a star brighter than Venus at its brightest seems to us; its disk would appear less than a twentieth as wide as our moon. Deimos is 12,500 miles from the surface of the planet and revolves in 30 hours and 18 minutes. It rises in the east but it remains above the horizon for about two and a half Martian days before setting in the west. Because these two small bodies are so close to Mars, they spend much of their time eclipsed, in the shadow of the planet and invisible to the hypothetical observer on the night side of Mars. When man travels to Mars, he may use one of these satellites or both as space stations ready-made for his purposes.

Beyond the orbit of Mars we find Jupiter, 483.3 millions of miles from the sun, traveling its 11.86-year orbit at an average speed of a little more than 8 miles per second. But on our way out to this giant planet we shall have to cross the belt of asteroids or minor planets that number certainly scores of thousands. Today about 2,000 are known, the largest less than 500 miles in diameter, the smallest perhaps only about a half-mile across. These are believed to be the debris remaining from a planet that, many millions of years ago, was shattered by some cataclysm.

Jupiter's diameter through the equator is 88,700 miles, through the poles only 82,800 miles; so the planet is quite flattened by its rapid rotation, 9 hours 50.5 minutes for objects at the equator. The apparent surface that we see is not solid; the features change and, in general, are in the form of belts or streaks parallel to the equator of the planet. This indicates that we see the top of a deep and dense atmosphere surrounding a smaller solid body. This is borne out by the fact that the mass of Jupiter is 318.0 times earth, yet its volume is 1317 times earth, leading to a mean density of only 1.33 times water.

With the spectroscope we find two noxious gases, ammonia and methane, in the Jovian atmosphere, but relatively small amounts of these materials could account for the spectrum of Jupiter; whereas hydrogen and helium, now believed to comprise the bulk of the upper atmosphere of the planet, would remain undetected. Closer to the sun, ammonia and methane, compounds of hydrogen with nitrogen and with carbon, respectively, would have been broken up for the most part, but out where Jupiter moves the temperature is about 200° F. below zero. Ice and frozen hydrogen and ammonia may lie on the surface of the solid planet deep below the visible surface of the atmosphere. We cannot know the diameter of the planet itself but, at the surface that we see, the surface gravity is 2.65 times that of earth and the velocity of escape is slightly more than 37 miles per second.

From Jupiter, two kinds of radio noise have been received, one consisting of sharp short bursts, the other of prolonged "rumbles" like the reverberation of thunder on earth. The sources of these signals are localized at certain spots of more or less permanent nature, long observed visually. If these sources are at the surface of the planet core, we may be able to determine the rotation period of the planet more precisely.

Jupiter is well supplied with satellites—a nice round dozen. The largest has a diameter of 3070 miles, about the size of the planet Mercury, and the runner-up is 2910 miles across. Two others have diameters of 1750 and 2000 miles, respectively, while the remaining eight range from perhaps 12 to 100 miles, too far away for accurate determination.

The satellites are arranged interestingly. One of them revolves in a period of less than 12 hours at a distance of only 68,000 miles—less than a Jupiter diameter—from the top of the atmosphere. The outermost satellite travels a very elliptical and erratic path almost 15 million miles from Jupiter, in a period of about 25 months. There is a group of three satellites at about 7.25 million miles from Jupiter, with periods of 251, 260, and 264 days, then the outer group of four averaging 14.2 million miles from the planet, with periods of 631, 692, 739, and 758 days. These outer four revolve around Jupiter in the "wrong" direction. So far, each body we have discussed revolves and rotates from west to east; these outer four Jovian satellites revolve from east to west.

We are concerned in this volume with space travel and, in some of this travel, we shall propose an orbit around the sun, to get to another planet or to revolve around it as an unnatural satellite while we examine it in detail. It is altogether possible that these four outermost companions of Jupiter are, in a sense, unnatural satellites—asteroids that, in the course of time, have swung out to Jupiter's orbit just as the planet passed by, and have been captured by the great gravitational field of this massive planet. Some have suggested that this stretches credulity too far, especially when we realize that the group of three satellites at about 7.25 million miles also seems irregular, demanding capturing of a further three asteroids. Perhaps two larger bodies were captured and, in the course of time, through causes unknown, were disrupted into three and four bodies, respectively. When space travelers get to Jupiter they may examine these and the other satellites closely, and discover whether they are all alike, essentially, or of very different composition.

Saturn, the planet with the beautiful flat ring system, unlike anything else we have ever discovered in the universe, revolves around the sun in a period of 29.46 years, traveling at 6 miles per second in an orbit with a mean radius of 886 millions of miles. Again we find methane in the atmosphere, because of this great distance from the sun; there is ammonia there, as well, but not as much as in Jupiter's atmosphere, because it is so cold that most of the ammonia must be in frozen form on the surface of the smaller planet which lies inside the atmospheric ball that measures about 75,000 miles through the equator and only 67,200 miles from pole to pole. This is the most flattened of all the planets, due to its rapid rotation—once around in 10 hours 14 minutes—and more than for Jupiter because of its largely atmospheric shell. The mass of Saturn is 95 times that of the earth; its density is only 0.69 times that of water, only an eighth as massive, per cubic foot, as the earth. The planet itself must be quite small. At the top of the atmosphere the surface gravity is 1.15 times that of the earth; the velocity of escape is 22 miles per second.

From rim to rim of the ring system the distance is 169,300 miles. The outer ring is 10,000 miles wide, then comes a clear gap of 1,750 miles, then the middle ring is 16,500 miles wide. It is brighter than the outer ring. Fading imperceptibly from its inner edge is the inner or "crepe" ring, so-called because it is quite transparent; this ring is 10,000 miles wide, its inner edge being 8,900 miles from the equator of Saturn. Thinner in proportion to its diameter than any sheet of paper, this system of annuli with the planet poised within it never fails to excite the admiration of those who view it through a telescope. And an astronomer who has the opportunity to observe the planet over many years never fails to be amazed to see Saturn apparently without rings when, each 15 years, the earth is lined up in the plane of the rings and they are edge-on. Except in large telescopes, the rings disappear for a few days, demonstrating their extreme thinness. With the spectroscope, it has been proved that the rings are made up of a vast myriad of particles of ice or, perhaps, solid particles covered with ice.

Saturn has nine satellites ranging in size from 3,000 to 150 miles. The largest one, at least, has an atmosphere of methane. The innermost satellite revolves around Saturn in a period of 22.6 hours, at a distance of 78,000 miles above the atmosphere of Saturn, only 31,000 miles from the outer rim of the ring system. The outermost satellite revolves in a period of 550 days, at a mean distance of 8 million miles from Saturn. This is more than 3½ times as far from the planet as the next most distant satellite; the period is 7 times as great as for that satellite. Moreover, this outermost companion of Saturn revolves the "wrong" way. These facts tend to indicate that this object, like the seven outer satellites of Jupiter and perhaps three others of Saturn, may be a captured body, and not one of Saturn's original retinue.

Beyond Saturn is Uranus, revolving in a period of 84 years at a speed of 4.2 miles per second in an orbit with mean radius of 1,783 millions of miles. The diameter of the object is 29,500 miles, the mass is 14.6 times that of the earth; the mean density is only 1.56 times that of water, so here again we have a smaller planet swathed in a deep, dense atmosphere containing methane. Frozen ammonia, water, and hydrogen may lie on the surface of the solid ball. The surface gravity is 0.96 that of the earth; the velocity of escape is about 14 miles per second.

Faint belts can be seen crossing the planet, telling us that, instead of having its axis almost perpendicular to its orbit, as is true of the other planets, Uranus has an axis of rotation lying almost in the plane of its orbit. Indeed, the inclination of the axis to the orbit is less than 8 degrees and in such a manner that the planet is said to rotate in the "wrong" direction, from east to west, in a period of 10.8 hours.

The five satellites of Uranus range in size from about 100 to 600 miles; they revolve in orbits that are practically circular and lie in the plane of the planet's equator, so they, too, must be thought of as revolving in the retrograde direction. The innermost one has an orbit with a radius of 76,000 miles and a period of 1.4 days; the outermost is at a distance of 364,000 miles from the center of Uranus and it revolves in a period of 13.5 days. It can be seen that we have here a much more compact system than those of Jupiter and Saturn.

Neptune, next beyond Uranus, was discovered in 1846 as a result of small deviations in the motion of Uranus. Its position was calculated and the planet was easily discovered. Neptune's mean distance from the sun is 2,793 millions of miles. Its almost circular orbit is traversed at an average speed of 3.4 miles per second, in a period of 165 years. The planet's diameter is 27,700 miles, the mass is 17.2 times that of the earth; the density is 2.27 times that of water, so here again we have a planet with a deep, dense atmosphere, but its solid bulk must be larger than that of Uranus. The surface gravity at the top of the atmosphere is 1.52 times that of earth; the escape velocity there is 15 miles per second. Methane, again, appears to be plentiful in the atmosphere. It rotates once in 15 hours 40 minutes.

Neptune's larger satellite revolves in a highly inclined orbit in the retrograde direction. This body has a diameter of 2,500 miles; its period of revolution is 5.88 days in a circular orbit with a mean radius of 220,000 miles. If it were not for the circular orbit and the large size of the satellite, it would be easy to believe that, because of its retrograde motion, we would be entitled to believe this to be a captured body. But it is more likely that Neptune's other satellite, despite its direct motion, is the captured one.

Its small diameter, about 200 miles, its high orbital eccentricity—largest for any satellite in the system—and its large mean distance from the planet—almost 3½ million miles—tempt us to this conclusion. When nearest Neptune, this object is only 820,000 miles from the center of the planet; at its greatest distance, it is 6,110,000 miles. The period of revolution is 359 days.

The outermost known planet, Pluto, has often been suspected to be an escaped satellite of Neptune. Its orbit is very different from that of any other major planet, with its high inclination or tilt with respect to the other orbits, and its high eccentricity, (greatest for any major planet). The mean distance of Pluto from the sun is 3,666 millions of miles, but when nearest the sun the distance is only 2,754 millions of miles—actually closer to the sun than Neptune's mean distance. When farthest from the sun, Pluto's distance is 4,578 million miles. The orbit is traversed in 248 years at an average speed of 2.94 miles per second. The inclination of the orbit is such that Pluto and Neptune can never collide, in spite of the fact that Pluto moves inside Neptune's orbit.

These are most of the facts on hand concerning Pluto. The planet is so distant that its physical characteristics are not well defined. Its diameter has been variously expressed between 3,600 and 4,900 miles. The mass is judged to be 0.9 that of the earth, thus leading to a density of more than 20 times water. While this might be possible for a planet largely composed of platinum or osmium, it is rather unlikely. The measurement of diameter, uncertain as it is, is probably much more reliable than the estimate of mass. Suppose we assume that Pluto's mean density is the same as that of the earth—5.52 times water. With a volume about a quarter of that of the earth, its mass also must be about a quarter of the earth's mass. This is a much more likely value than that given earlier, and one that can be assumed to be the upper limit for the mass of this planet out on the fringe of our system.

This does put us in a dilemma, of course, when we recall that Pluto was discovered in 1930 as a result of a many-years-long search for the planet that was disturbing the motion of Neptune, itself discovered because of perturbations of Uranus. Two astronomers, W. H. Pickering and Percival Lowell, independently predicted the place of the unknown planet with considerable accuracy, the former from as yet unexplained residuals in the motion of Uranus, the latter from the perturbations of Neptune. Some time after Pluto was discovered, the great mathematical astronomer E. W. Brown showed, at least to his own satisfaction and to that of many others, that Pluto was too small to have enough mass to have perturbed either Neptune or Uranus, and that the source or sources of the disturbances must be looked for elsewhere. If he was correct (and it would appear

from the measures of diameter of the planet that he
may have been) then we must count the discovery of
Pluto was too small to have enough mass to have
of astronomy—far more significant, but of the same
nature, as the discovery by another astronomer of a
bright new comet in exactly the same position as that
of a very faint comet that he had been following
night after night.

From variations in its light, Pluto's rotation period has been determined as 6.39 days. The temperature of 400° F. below zero might lead us to conclude
that atmospheric materials as we know them would
all be solidified on the surface of the planet. Pluto
is now approaching its aphelion; about 135 years
from now it will be at perihelion, closer to the sun
than Neptune, and perhaps the higher temperature
then will vaporize some of the materials and we
can say that Pluto has an atmosphere, and detect its
components. Before that time, of course, we may
have been able to do a better job on the planet when
we observe it with telescopes on the moon or on
Mars established during some of our early space
voyages.

From our census, it should be obvious that only
two of the planets, Venus and Mars, hold much
promise as profitable targets for tomorrow. Of
Venus, we know very little except that it should be
possible to exist, inside space suits, on its surface—if
it has a solid surface. Mars, we know, is all solid

surface, except that its surface, like that of the moon, may have a layer of dust. On both planets, protection from radiations from space will be afforded, and atmospheric pressure to make us feel comfortable in light or even partial space suits; although we shall find it necessary to provide oxygen for breathing, and to dispose of carbon dioxide and water exhaled. Average temperature conditions should not be impossible on either planet, although some protection against high temperatures on Venus and low temperatures on Mars may be in order.

To plunge into the deep, cold atmospheres of dangerous gases on the outer planets is probably out of the question, but some of their satellites may be occupied briefly while closer examinations of the planets are pursued. And it will certainly be a high adventure, albeit probably an unprofitable one, to set down on the innermost planet, Mercury. There are people who have climbed Mt. Everest or who have walked across Antarctica, just to show it can be done. It is doubtful that this kind of ambition will ever be bred out of the race of men; and to be "first on Mercury" or on Jupiter or Pluto may still have an appeal, regardless of practical gain to be had.

CHAPTER 15

The Noah's Ark of Space

Millennia ago when sentient man first turned his eyes to the sky and gazed on the stars, fear and awe may have been his reactions. As time went on and man began to learn the nature of the objects in the sky, the fear was displaced by intelligent wonder. Man was still awed by the boundless space that stretched overhead, and some of our predecessors must have asked the questions: Is there life elsewhere in the universe? Are there other creatures like or unlike ourselves on the surfaces of other planets which must abound in the sky?

Only recently has man been able to comprehend the nature of other objects in space and to draw conclusions. The astronomer has taken a census not only of the objects in the sky but also of their compositions. Without knowing how our own world came into being, he believes that this world is not unique, but that in space there is almost an infinity of worlds, with some of them possessing life, perhaps like our own. Statistically, these conclusions always can be drawn. The next logical question now is: Will we ever find out about these other worlds? The answer is an intriguing one. Let's examine it.

As has been indicated earlier in this volume, the author believes that man will reach the moon by the year 1980. Once he has landed there, he will have enough power available to use the materials of the moon much as the same kinds of materials are used on earth. On the moon, he will be able to construct enormous space ships to explore the solar system and even, perhaps, to explore the regions around some of the other stars. The low gravitational pull at the moon's surface makes this body the only logical base for outer space explorations.

Astronomers have become interested in certain faint stars whose positions have been measured more or less continuously with very high precision. These stars appear to move along wavy paths and the astronomer knows, from Newton's laws of motion (see Chapter 2) and from experience, that nothing but the gravitational attraction of another body can make a star deviate from straight-line motion.

The author has often illustrated this point by asking his listeners to imagine the motion of two bodies through space as analogous to that observed in an Argentinian bola thrown through the air. Let's imagine the two balls to be of unequal size. Then the path taken by the whirling pair will be more nearly that of the massive ball, but even this more important one of the pair will be seen to be describing a wavy path through the air, the waves being produced by the pull of the smaller ball. A star and a massive, invisible companion perform in the same way.

From the size of the wiggle in the path of the star, the astronomer can determine the relative mass of the invisible companion. When this is done for one of the two visible stars that make up the double system of 61 Cygni, the visible star has a wavy motion that tells us that the dark companion has a mass of about one-sixtieth that of the bright star. This is the least massive of these invisible companions so far found.

The discovery of the existence of this dark star or companion and the evaluation of its mass is very difficult, so the important point to be brought up is this: If there is an invisible companion one-sixtieth as massive as the visible star, why can there not be other companions with even smaller masses? The astronomer knows no reason why there cannot be; the mechanism that gives rise to one companion can give rise to smaller ones. So astronomers conclude that planetary systems in the sky, far from being exceptions, may be the rule.

With spectroscopes attached to telescopes, astronomers find that the same chemical elements found in our part of space, in and near the sun, and on earth, are scattered throughout the whole visible universe, and in just about the same proportions as we find here at home. Also, in space we find many stars quite like our sun in size and temperature, thus emitting about the same amount and the same types of radiation as our sun. With conditions elsewhere so closely paralleling those in our part of space, it is inconceivable to this writer that there could not be an enormous host of living creatures elsewhere in the universe.

The question then becomes: Will we ever find out? There may be devised some as yet unheard-of technique for answering this question, but the answer may involve the use of a giant rocket ship which we may call a celestial "Noah's Ark"—a name given this concept by others at various times.

Visualize a giant space ship of the distant future; its weight might be of the order of a million tons, its material fabricated from the ores and minerals of the moon, its path through space originating on the moon. This Ark would be intricately compartmented; it must contain a complete civilization.

There would be schools, libraries, universities, nurseries, hospitals, farms—both animal and vegetable—and food-packaging plants. There would be laboratories, factories, machine shops, repair facilities of every conceivable kind. The entire company and equipment would be such that the skills of each man would contribute to the welfare of the whole group. Here would be the perfect socialistic state; everything would be subjugated to the good and the will of the state.

The energy sources in the Ark would furnish not only the power for the ship itself but also all needs of the living cargo. During most of the long voyage through space the ship would be so far from the stars that their radiation would be of no value. From nuclear or thermonuclear reactions, as far as we can foresee today, all radiation needs must be served. Either a tremendous store of U-235 or plutonian must be available, or an equally large store of heavy hydrogen to be converted into helium. In either case, there must be the facilities for performing the conversion into energy and for distributing to the proper places in the proper form.

The radiation fed to the plants to keep them alive and reproducing must simulate sunlight; these plants, of course, must feed the animals as well as the humans, so the latter will have the meat of the animals for food. It is possible, of course, that by the time of the launching of the Ark researches here on earth will have resulted in palatable and nourishing food sources which today we only suspect may sometime be available, in almost unlimited quantities, starting from a small supply.

While this provision for maintaining a civilization is one involving stupendous engineering difficulties, let us pass on into a real realm of fantasy necessitated by the length of time it will take to reach the stars. It is believed that a speed of about 10 miles per second will be satisfactory for interplanetary voyages, in our own system. We may have to cover some billions of miles in the long trips, but with about 31,500,000 seconds in a year we can cover about a third of a billion miles in a year. Thus the 10 miles per second available in the near future will be adequate for trips to be undertaken in the near future. But the story is different when we raise our sights beyond the solar system and think of moving off to the nearest stars.

The nearest stars are in a system in the Southern Hemisphere in the constellation Centaurus—about 25 millions of millions of miles away. We call this distance 4⅓ light-years, because light, traveling at 186,300 miles per second, requires 4⅓ years to get from these stars to us. But our first goals may be 61 Cygni, or 70 Ophiuchi, stars about twice as far away, but known to have companions with a mass intermediate between red dwarfs and Jupiter. The speed of 10 miles per second is seen to be wholly inadequate; the trip one-way would take about 160,000 years, and double that for a round trip—a ridiculously large span of time.

We are in the realm of not impossible fantasy here,

so let's imagine that in the distant future it may be possible to accelerate a space ship to a speed of 10,000 miles per second, about 1000 times as great as that sufficient for travel to the nearer planets. Now our round trip to 61 Cygni will take only 320 years— a few lifetimes, but not too inconceivable; the span from the landing of the Pilgrims to today.

In the Ark, humans will travel for generation after generation. The original voyagers will take off, have their children (by a rigidly-controlled quota) and live their lives to die off and let the next generation take over to guide the ship to its destination. Again and again, succeeding generations will take over to carry forward the aims of the expedition. Finally, the Ark may reach one of those stars for which we have found invisible companions.

When it does, the inhabitants of the ship will explore the planetary system searching for the answer to the question of other life in the universe. If they should discover living creatures, there will be no signal that can be sent back to appraise the earth of that fact. The only way to get the information back to earth is to come back to earth. The generation that returns to earth will be one to which the earth is almost a legend. Advances through the centuries, both on the ship and on earth, may make it difficult for adjustments to be made for living on earth.

It is conceivable that some of the space travelers

from earth may prefer to remain on a distant planet around another star. While it is certain that the original voyagers will be willing to embark from earth, knowing full well that they will live out their lives and die en route, we cannot be sure that all of the succeeding generations will be willing to do so; some of them may want to remain on any substantial body that comes their way. Perhaps, while some earthmen colonize distant planets, some of the natives of the distant planets may be persuaded to start the voyage back home. There are many interesting possibilities when we begin to engage in this kind of speculation.

We have blithely spoken of speeds of the order of 10,000 miles per second, yet this very speed may be the one factor that will prevent the Ark from reaching its destination. Today the astronomer has a fair idea of the number of small particles that abound between the planets and, even, between the stars. Most of these are small, no larger than a grain of sand, but they enter the earth's atmosphere with speeds up to almost 45 miles per second. Such a speed gives them great energy. A tiny particle moving at a speed of 25 miles per second has about as much energy as a high-powered rifle bullet. One twice as massive, at the same speed, has twice the energy. Even in the short trips in the neighborhood of the earth, we know there are these small bodies that are potential hazards; for the extended space trips, at high velocities, the hazard may be too great.

Some scientists have suggested that these particles are strictly solar system members, and that they thin out or are even non-existent between the stars. Dr. Fred L. Whipple has advanced evidence that the space between the stars is a deep freeze which houses the comets that move around the sun. Disturbed by the gravitational fields of other stars, the comets embark on their journeys in toward the sun and, once having got into our system, are captured by the planets and forced to remain as permanent members.

In England, Mr. J. G. Tyror, acting on a suggestion by Dr. R. A. Lyttleton, has only recently shown all but the short-period comets (whose orbits have been distorted by the large planets) to have come from a direction in space which is almost precisely that in which the sun is moving with respect to its neighbors, as though they had been swept up by the sun from interstellar space. This is an interesting observation which requires much more study. The nuclei of comets are composed of tiny particles in a matrix of hydrogen ices—methane, ammonia, and water. Thus out in space, far beyond the solar system, we must accept the existence of particles similar to those near the earth, presenting a critical problem in long-distance space travel.

When two bodies collide, it makes no difference whether the energy of the collision is due to the motion of one body, the other, or to that of both.

Let's begin with a particle of matter about the size of a grain of sugar, weighing about 0.004 gram. If we let m be its mass, v its velocity, then the kinetic energy of its motion is K.E. $= \frac{1}{2} m v^2$. Suppose we use 10 miles per second for the velocity, converting it into feet per second; let's convert the mass in grams to mass in pounds, so our answer will come out in foot-pounds. The result is 12,500 foot-pounds for the kinetic energy of a grain of sugar traveling at 10 miles per second.

But we have spoken of a speed of 10,000 miles per second for the Ark; even with this speed, we faced a round trip of 320 years. This speed is 1000 times as great as the one in our example above, so the kinetic energy (which goes up as the *square* of the velocity) becomes a million times as great; the grain of sugar, at 10,000 miles per second, has a kinetic energy of 12,500 million foot-pounds. Perhaps we can explain this in simpler terms.

A rifle bullet, weighing perhaps an ounce, travels with a speed of 3,000 feet per second; the kinetic energy is about 300,000 foot-pounds. Our grain of sugar has about 400,000 times as much kinetic energy! A projectile as heavy as a block of iron slightly less than two feet on an edge, traveling at 3,000 feet per second (the speed of a rifle bullet), has the same kinetic energy, approximately, as our grain of sugar traveling at 10,000 miles per second.

Because of the danger to a celestial Noah's Ark from such impacts, there have been suggestions that perhaps a conventionally fabricated space ship is not the answer, at least for these trips at highest speeds.

In our system, largely between the orbits of Mars and Jupiter, there revolve around the sun an enormous number of small planets, called asteroids. Astronomers believe that, a long time ago, there was another planet in our system which, for unknown reasons, shattered. The fragments are the asteroids, ranging in size from almost 500 miles in diameter to known bodies less than a mile across. One suggestion has been that an asteroid might make an ideal Noah's Ark in space.

Large ships fabricated on the moon could carry us out to the asteroid belt where we would select the object we want to convert. We would then hollow it out, compartment it, and establish our civilization in it. Nuclear rockets could be installed on all faces of the object.

Because of the relatively small size of the asteroid, the gravitational pull will be small, so it may be desirable to establish some form of artificial surface gravity, if the asteroid is not already spinning. We can produce any period of rotation we wish, by using rockets angled for the purpose. Inside the asteroid, voyagers would walk and work with their heads toward the center of the object. Air locks might give access to certain observation posts hollowed out of the shell, on the surface of the asteroid. These might be covered with thick sheets of transparent plastic strong enough to stand the impacts of transient particles in space. In the event of damage, the air locks would prevent any catastrophe to the whole expedition. A shell perhaps a few hundred feet thick would be the armoring for the main chambers of the Ark; this much of the original surface of the asteroid would be relatively untouched in the excavation process. The material removed will contain ores that can be used for fabrication of necessities of the expedition; it is even possible that some rocks containing water of crystallization will be found, from which the water can be extracted for use.

There are two ways in which we can get away from the sun's gravitational field and get to the stars. Both methods involve the use of a "gravitational whip." One way which has been discussed for a long time has been the moving in toward the sun and letting the sun swing the asteroid off into space in a hyperbolic path. The other method, the result of some rather recent work of Krafft Ehricke, uses the planet Jupiter as the whip. Ehricke has shown that, when a space ship approaches Jupiter, the gravitational field of the big planet is so strong as to attract the ship to its surface. If, however, the approach is precisely right and the speed is precisely right, the gravitational field of the planet can act as a slingshot to project the Ark into a hyperbolic path to the stars. Thus we have the means whereby power need not be used continuously to escape the sun's field. All that is needed is the power to maneuver the Ark to the right spot at the right time with the right speed and direction, and the Jovian gravitational field can get the Ark well started on its way, using power to build up the speed to whatever value is desired or feasible.

The captured asteroid as a space ship has definite merit, certainly as far as protection from missile hazards in space is concerned. Using this type of Ark, man will be able to get away from earth to the other stars.

CHAPTER 16

Longer Life in Space

Legend has it that centuries ago the emperor Frederick Barbarossa, he of the fiery red beard, went to sleep in front of a marble table to await his country's call to help. Once every hundred years he awoke and bade his page to see whether the ravens were still circling overhead.

When the page reported that the ravens were still flying, indicating that the propitious moment had not yet arrived, the master sank back into a sleep which lasted another century. The legend continues that when the fiery beard has grown until it completes its third circle around the marble table, the ravens will cease to flutter, the battle trumpets will sound and the emperor will arise from his enchanted sleep to lead his people to freedom.

Thus, in legend, we are told of the man who awakens once a century to view the world. But the truth is, in some cases, stranger than fiction and today comes the exciting prospect of a human being's leaving the earth to go to some faraway place and return in a century without aging 100 years. While Barbarossa actually aged in the time he was asleep, the modern-day Barbarossa will age but little.

The reason behind this exciting speculation is that in the sky lies the fountain of youth. With motion in the sky can come perpetual youth; motion may turn out to be the elixir of life.

Does this sound bizarre—fantastic? It does. Yet some scientists look on this as a startling result of one of Einstein's greatest contributions to science—the special theory of relativity.

This theory, conceived more than fifty years ago, has opened the flood-gates of speculation and has led to dramatic and intriguing conjectures concerning the effects on a human being who is moving through space with extraordinarily high speeds, something that today is in the realm of possibility.

One aspect of the special theory of relativity relates changes in mass, length, and time to increase in speed. As a consequence of this theory, it can be shown mathematically that, as speed increases, the length of a body in the direction of its motion decreases, the mass increases and time slows down as judged by earth clocks. At the speed of light—

186,300 miles per second—length becomes zero, mass becomes infinite, and time stands still.

It must be understood that these changes in dimension, mass, and time must be judged by an observer fixed in the frame of reference we are using to designate the velocity of the moving body. We are interested here only in the slowdown or dilation of time, which is normally imperceptible because motions on earth or even in the universe are so slow as compared with the velocity of light. Only at tremendous speeds can even the most sensitive of instruments be expected to detect this effect.

Any doubts as to the validity of this theory have been at least partially dissipated by laboratory experiments and observations in nature. For example, when cyclotrons are used to accelerate up to a large fraction of the speed of light the particles used to bombard the nuclei of atoms, to change or transmute them into new elements, a substantial increase in mass of the particles is observed. In fact, so pronounced is this increase that the cyclotrons had to compensate for this relativistic change of mass so that the electric "kick" could be synchronized with the particles; only then could the cyclotrons operate satisfactorily at high energies.

High above the dense lower atmosphere of the earth, primary cosmic rays collide with particles of air and shatter them, creating many other particles that are the secondary cosmic rays. Some of these are short-lived. At an altitude of 25 miles above the surface, mu-mesons are produced. These are tiny particles, of mass much less than that of the nucleus of the hydrogen atom. They have been produced in the laboratory, and their life-span is only two millionths of a second. Now, they come cascading down from heights of 25 miles and, if they travel with the speed of light, it should take them about 130 millionths of a second. We perceive them at the earth's surface, so they must have persisted for at least 65 times their normal lifetimes; they should have died out in the first 0.4 mile of the path. The fact that they don't is linked with the expansion of their time-scale due to their high speeds.

For many years there has been general acceptance of the time dilation aspect of the special theory of relativity. Only recently has any opposition to these concepts been advanced. At this moment an acrimonious wrangle has been triggered among distinguished scientists of outstanding ability. The launching of earth satellites and the imminence of rockets to the moon have lifted the question out of the purely academic realm and have demanded a practical appraisal.

In the staid and proper *Nature,* a ranking magazine of science published in Great Britain, a series of provocative articles has appeared in which two articulate astronomers, Professors W. M. McCrae and Herbert Dingle, have publicly debated the question of remaining young while traveling at high speeds. While both agree that with increased speed the clocks of the space traveler will slow down, the interpretation of the slowdown in a practical way is the basis of the controversy.

Prof. McCrae considers the heart as a form of clock. When the speed is high enough there will be a perceptible slowing down of the heart so that the body metabolism will also slow down and thus we will live slower and longer. Prof. Dingle contends that this interpretation is a violation of what he calls "common sense."

Why anyone should use a term like common sense, in light of the phenomenal progress in the fields of electronics, atomic bombs, and other nuclear devices, is difficult to comprehend. Today it must be admitted that common sense is the usual, but the unusual also has an insidious way of becoming reality.

Scientists like Prof. Dingle, who do not believe that youth can be preserved with fast motions, argue that the only thing that counts in this theory is velocities. They point out that only a relative motion is involved—that the earth is moving away from the space traveler at precisely the same speed with which the space ship is moving away from the earth. Therefore, if the clocks on the space ship are slowing down with respect to those on the earth, by the same token the clocks on the earth are slowing down with respect to the space traveler. Thus, if the space traveler leaves the earth at great speed and returns at some distant date, the clocks on both the space ship and the earth will precisely coincide and there will be no aging of the "earth people" with respect to the space traveler. They say that the relative velocities make for perfectly symmetrical conditions, and thus it is impossible to differentiate between the space traveler and those who remain on earth. Therefore, they contend, it is ridiculous to assume that one has any special property not possessed by the other. Thus there can be no difference in ages.

To this, Prof. McCrae and his fellow scientists say, "Nonsense!" They hold that the space ship is being accelerated away from the earth. The space travelers are the ones who are doing the moving, by virtue of this acceleration. Therefore, if they are accelerated, then their clocks will slow down and the people on the accelerated vehicle will live longer. They hold that the frame of reference is centered on the earth and it is the space ship that moves in this frame of reference. The earth is stationary in this system so that symmetry of motions does not exist. The consequence of this asymmetry is that the aging process of the space travelers will be retarded.

Thus the controversy rages.

Medical men also have been involved in this

controversy. A team of doctors from Harvard University has pondered this from the metabolic point of view and concludes that there would be no difference in ages between the space traveler and the earth people. Rather passionately these doctors dispute the findings of one of Dr. Einstein's colleagues, Philipp Frank. Of Dr. Frank's conclusions, they say, "He compares this slowing of life's processes, due to an increased uniform motion, to the slowing which occurs at a reduced body temperature. So the conclusion given is that the motion of the space ship inflicts a kind of hibernation on its passengers and they arrive home awakening, like the Sleeping Beauty and her household, to find a new generation on earth while they themselves are but little older."

The medical men probe the ability of the body to withstand conditions which are alien and perhaps lethal to a human being. This slowing down of time to them means hibernation, and hibernation means a lowering of the body temperature. They claim that a drop of 11 or 12 degrees brings unconciousness and a possibility of death. Certainly the performance of the individual would be critically affected if there should be hibernation.

These doctors, like Prof. Dingle, reject the idea partially on the grounds of "common sense," because common sense insists that a sort of hibernation is the logical consequence of this situation. Therefore, in their paper, as in Prof. Dingle's writings, they insist on the symmetry of velocities of the space ship and the earth. And like Prof. Dingle they prefer to ignore the acceleration of the space ship to get it up to the high speeds. It is the opinion of many scientists, strongly shared by this writer, that acceleration cannot be ignored. Only by permitting it to enter the picture can a definitive answer be found.

If the special theory of relativity is completely valid, and at this time there is a strong feeling that it is, then at some future date man will come face to face with the possibility of a long life span. In this speculation we are not just juggling time sequences. The human aging process would be slowed. It can be explained in the following manner.

Imagine the human body as a clock of sorts. The balance wheel may have its counterpart in the heart. Thus the beating of the heart would measure time. As the space traveler moves at high speed, the slowing down of the clocks on the space ship would be simultaneously accompanied by a slowing down of the heart in its beating. The normal heart beats 72 times a minute. A sufficiently high speed would make the heart beat only 72 times an hour!

Run the speed up still higher and the heart may beat but once a day. But remember the unit of time we are using is the unit of time as measured on the earth. The crew on the rocket ship would be completely unaware of the slowing down of their clocks.

If they took their pulses using the clocks on the space ship, the rate would still be 72 a minute.

The metabolism of the body would be retarded until the functioning of the body practically ceased. In that way the body could survive for inordinately long travel periods.

This time dilation can be easily computed. We simply begin with a number, 186,300 miles a second —the speed of light. Now if a space ship can be accelerated until it attains a speed of 167,700 miles a second, approximately 90 per cent of the speed of light, the traveler would age but 10 years for a trip which the stay-at-homes on earth said had taken 23 years.

For those who would like to compute some of these times below we find the formula:*

$$E = \frac{T}{\sqrt{1 - \dfrac{v^2}{c^2}}}$$

in which E = interval on the earth clock (and also the interval on the traveler's clock as judged by an observer on earth.)

       T = interval on the traveler's clock as judged by the traveler

       v = Velocity of the space traveler as referred to the earth

       c = Velocity of light, 186,300 miles per second

for the space traveler moving at 167,700 miles per second, to find the change in one second the equation looks like this:

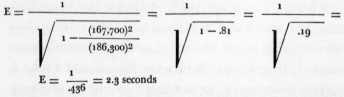

$$E = \frac{1}{\sqrt{1 - \dfrac{(167,700)^2}{(186,300)^2}}} = \frac{1}{\sqrt{1 - .81}} = \frac{1}{\sqrt{.19}} =$$

$$E = \frac{1}{.436} = 2.3 \text{ seconds}$$

* The pure relativist will probably be shocked by this notation but the mathematics student will perhaps find it more understandable.

Therefore, a second on the earth would be less than a half-second on the space ship. So a trip which lasted 23 earth years would find the space travelers aged by 10 years.

If the speed of the traveler goes up to 184,400 miles per second, 99 per cent of the speed of light, a 10-year trip for the traveler will take 71 earth years. A speed of 186,100 miles per second, about 99.9 per cent of the speed of light, would make the 10-year trip seem to have lasted more than 224 years. At 99.99 per cent of the speed of light, the trip that lasted 1,000 years by earth clocks will have aged the travelers only 14 years. The closer the speed of the ship approaches the speed of light, the more time is slowed until, at that limiting speed, time stops.

A good bit of stimulating speculation has centered around the behavior of a space traveler traveling with a large fraction of the speed of light.

In my office I can walk a distance of 60 feet, without exertion, in about 10 seconds. If an observer on earth could see me in a space ship traveling at 186,-000 miles per second, he would clock me over this same 60-foot distance in about 170 earth-seconds; to him it would appear that I would be performing in very slow, slow-motion. Similarly, all my other movements would seem slowed down, as viewed from earth. Eating a meal, which might normally take a half-hour on earth, would seem to use up the best part of a day, as viewed from earth.

Even my reflexes and automatic actions would be expanded in this weird fashion. If I see something out of the corner of my eye, normally about a tenth of a second is required to perceive it. In a space ship traveling at about 186,000 miles per second, this interval would be judged from earth to be almost 1¾ seconds; a further 17 seconds, instead of the normal one second, would seem to be required for me to recognize what I saw. All of my functions, as clocked on earth, would seem decelerated; to me on the space ship they would appear quite normal.

In essence, those who speculate on what the future will bring are, in bold imagination, embarking on a trip through time. Let us assume that in 1928 a 28-year-old couple departed on a 30-year trip in which they traveled at 185,370 miles a second. Let us further assume that they left behind a one-year-old daughter. While the clocks on earth were ticking away the passage of 30 years, the clocks in the space ship would seem to have marked off only three years. The 28-year-old couple, on their return, would seem only 31 years old.

Every woman loves to hear the flattering remark when she is with her daughter that they look almost like sisters. If our couple should go out to dinner in 1958 taking their daughter with them, then truly could the remark be made, "Why, you look like sisters, not like mother and daughter!" Mother would be 31 years old, just the age of her daughter.

This one time the flattery would not be empty. If the women are really serious about staying young— and what woman isn't?—here may be the solution to this longing.

What wonderful events and developments would be seen to have taken place in those "three years"! What a spectacular scientific panorama would have unfolded!

When the couple left the earth in 1928, the atomic bomb, the hydrogen bomb, and nuclear energy were unheard-of except in the wildest of science fiction stories. The antibiotics were unknown. While it is true that Dr. Robert Goddard fired his first liquid-fueled rocket in 1926, even the most optimistic of forward-looking scientists would have completely rejected the possibility of an earth satellite by 1957. In 1928 the radio set was big, impressive, and mysterious. Today radio is commonplace, and sets as small as match boxes can be built. Television in those days was an experimental curiosity, almost a vision. Today it is the most powerful influence on human affairs ever conceived. Radar was unknown then; today radar techniques probe the universe. A weapon that killed a few-score people was a horrendous instrument of destruction. In 1958 a single well-placed weapon could wipe out a million people. In 1928 the universe was small and our ignorance of it was great. Today, while our ignorance is almost as great, the universe has expanded to almost inconceivable dimensions.

Thus the world would have changed in the short "three-year" trip of our couple. Now, suppose the couple were to leave on another trip of the same duration. What would the earth be like when they returned, only three years older, in 1988? What changes will have occurred? What will be the design of our homes, our lighting, our heating, our communications, our foods, our patterns for living? These are the speculations that spring to our minds as we appraise the consequences of Einstein's special theory of relativity.

If the application of this theory does slow down the aging process, will we become aware of it soon? Can we look forward to a definitive solution to this question in the near future? The answer is no. While within perhaps 20 years man may travel to a space station and thus attain a speed of five miles per second, this is so slow that in a life span of 100 years the inhabitants of the space station would gain but one second over those remaining on earth. Only in the distant future when trips to the outer reaches of the solar system or even to the stars are contemplated can the effects become appreciable enough to answer this question.

And if the answer should demonstrate the complete validity of this theory, then perhaps the earth is due for a staggering social upheaval in which people will demand space travel as a sort of elixir of life. For then, as Prof. Dingle points out, we may find "some patriarch embarking on a trip to the Andromeda Nebula in an attempt to outlive his great-great-grand-daughter."

The Other Side of the Moon

In chapter 11 we discovered why the moon always kept the same side toward the earth. We also learned why we peek over the edge of the moon so that we see 59 per cent of it, while the other 41 per cent is always invisible to us.

The immediate future will see successful moon reconnaissance probes. At that time we may learn the exact nature of the other side. The first pictures to be relayed to the earth will disclose little detail, for the first scanning devices will be primitive ones in which the necessary resolution will be unavailable. However, the subsequent probes will reveal more and more detail, until finally we will learn the precise nature of the other side.

Astronomers have long speculated as to what was

on the other side of the moon. At least one astronomer—Dr. H. Percy Wilkins, Director of the British
Astronomical's Lunar Section—has presented a map
of what it should look like. He indicates that a de-
pression on one side of the earth is usually com-
pensated by an elevation of the land mass on the opposite side. Applying this terrestrial principle to the
moon, he has established that some seas and ray centers must be present on the other side of the moon.
His arguments are certainly plausible, and his "Con-
jectural Aspect of the Moon's Other Side" violates
no scientific principle.

The author came across Dr. Wilkins' excellent
book in 1954 and has spent a good bit of time thinking about the moon. This has led to his closed ecological cycle on the moon and has also indicated that
the other side of the moon may be reconstructed
through a statistical analysis.

A photograph of the full moon discloses that fully
half the surface is made up of the "maria" or seas.
The other half of the visible side is composed of
pitted areas or craters with an incredibly rough
topography.

To this observer the aspect of the other side is
highly dependent on how these seas came into being. While the complete answer to this may not
emerge until man sets foot on the moon, it is possible to draw some pertinent conclusions.

The consensus is that several billion years ago a

giant meteor, or planetesimal, struck the moon at the place today called Mare Imbrium. The planetesimal was supposedly from 125 to 200 miles in diameter and struck the moon with a nominal speed which Dr. Harold Urey puts at about 1.5 miles a second. Dr. Urey picks this speed as an upper limit, for, had the speed been greater, the resulting explosion would have given rise to a symmetrical pattern to the Mare Imbrium region which is not apparent.

A body of this size moving with this speed possesses a tremendous amount of kinetic energy, that is, energy of motion. If the planetesimal was 125 miles in diameter with a density of 3.5 and moving with a speed of 1.5 miles a second, the energy released on impact would have been 4.15×10^{32} ergs. Dr. George Gamow indicates that an erg represents the energy of a small mosquito flying across a room. Yet, the energy of impact suggested above is equal to 460 billion atomic bombs.

To represent this in another way, divide the entire earth into city blocks. Then, says Dr. Urey, if one atomic bomb were exploded on every city block we would have expended the same amount of energy as was given up when the planetesimal struck the moon.

Precisely what happened at the time of impact no one knows. But this much is known: There was a tremendous amount of energy available as the kinetic energy of motion. This was converted to heat, and the result was the formation of a tremendous pool of lava which flowed from the Mare Imbrium region to form, to the east, the Mare Nubium and the Oceanus Procellarum.

The lava flowed to the west to form the Mare Serenitatis, Mare Tranquillitatis, the Mare Foecunditatis and the sliver we call Mare Nectaris. If other seas existed prior to this event—and there is some evidence to indicate this—they were submerged in the flood of lava which flowed from the impact point.

Prior meteoric impacts could have thrown up mountain ranges and the lava flows would have innundated these as well as some of the larger craters bordering this region. The flooding of the Mare Imbrium floor is indicated by isolated peaks still found in that region.

Violent explosions ripped along the surface through mountains to create the valleys and rifts which can be traced back to the impact point in the Mare Imbrium. Away from the seas around the south pole, we find the old moon whose craters antedate the Mare Imbrium catastrophe.

If what has been said makes sense, we can say that nowhere else on this side of the moon was there an impact by a planetesimal of the size that struck the Mare Imbrium region. Certainly if there was we would see it and no comparable area is visible.

There are several other small seas on the moon which we see when the moon librates. But in every case, except one, we see the small sea in its entirety. Thus, it becomes apparent that the only region where another planetesimal could have hit the other side to create a large sea area similar to the Mare Imbrium is directly in the center of the other side. Unless it hit dead center we would see the edges of the seas coming around the limb.

The odds of a planetesimal hitting directly in the center of the other side are so small as not to merit serious consideration. Thus, we come to the conclusion that the other side of the moon is wholly unlike the side facing the earth. But it does appear possible to obtain a statistical picture of it.

A careful look at the near side shows that the southern half is composed principally of the old pre-mare areas, unaffected by the encroachment of lava flows from the impact center. Thus, we should expect to see the other side as made up of material which comprises the southern half of the visible moon. But what sort of craters, how many and what kind of seas should we find?

To arrive at this picture the moon is divided into approximately northern and southern regions. Then the areas of the moon which were obviously the result of the lava flows are traced. This ratio of the old moon to the total southern half we will call the "deficiency factor" and this turns out to be 79.6 per cent.

Then the craters are counted on the whole moon

which have diameters from 20 to 29 miles, from 30 to 39 miles, from 40 to 49 miles, from 50 to 59 miles, from 60 to 79 miles, from 80 to 99 miles and finally from 100 to 146 miles. The same range of crater sizes were counted in the southern half. The ratio of the two gave a number which may be called the "rectification factor." This factor is used to eliminate the effect of the seas on the northern hemisphere.

By taking the number of craters of a given size in the southern half and multiplying by two we have the number for the entire side of the moon. This number multiplied by the deficiency and rectification factors yielded the number of craters on the other side of the moon of a given diameter.

The total number of craters 20 miles or over in diameter on the side of the moon facing us is 227. However, the total for the other side is 395 craters or more. Thus, the absence of the large sea areas on the other side of the moon almost doubles the number of craters.

Examination of the earth side and the limb due to librations discloses many of the smaller seas like Mare Crisium, Mare Marginus, the Mare Smythii, Mare Humboltianum, etc.

From the presence of these and the total area they occupy we may draw the conclusion that there should be four or perhaps five small maria on the side of the moon we cannot see.

Thus, from a purely statistical study it is possible

to derive the total number of craters and the maria that should be present on the other side of the moon. Whether the numbers are precise we cannot know; we can only indicate the magnitude of this array. The positions of the craters and the maria we also cannot know. This will remain a mystery until we get around to the other side of the moon.

Very shortly a lunar probe will start for the moon and the necessary guidance will be available to propel it into an orbit to circle the moon. By means of complex reconnaissance equipment, pictures will be taken, which will relay this intelligence to the earth. Only then can we determine the validity of this study.

Education and Training for Space Engineers

At this moment, thousands of promising high school and college students are sitting over their books looking off into space and wondering: How can I get into the space flight field? Am I taking the right courses to train me to become a part of the greatest adventure in the history of man? Whom can I talk to to guide me in this field?

This is a serious problem, because there are all too few sources of good answers to these questions. And, while the future will bring a stabilization to a program of this kind, at this time very little is known about what is needed and very few institutions have given serious attention to the demands of the future generations of students.

These questions have been asked of the author

many times, and from his own experience and from conversations with ranking educators in many parts of the country he has been able to crystallize his own thinking somewhat.

It is only natural that the background of the one answering these questions should be projected prominently into the picture. The author's background influences his conception of what is needed and what can be done. His high school years were spent at an excellent institution, Central High School in Philadelphia; here his later training was given a good foundation. Later, he attended the Drexel Institute of Technology, receiving a Bachelor's degree in Mechanical Engineering. After working for several years in astronomy at The Franklin Institute, he attended the University of Pennsylvania, receiving Master's and Doctor's degrees in Astronomy.

The author firmly believes that the proper education for participation in the space age must combine the practical and theoretical aspects in a completely integrated fashion. For example, the student should be a capable craftsman and the place to start developing into one is in the high school. Most schools have mechanics arts courses that permit the student to "get his hands dirty." He will make all sorts of little things, but the important part of this type of training is not necessarily that he become a skilled mechanic. Instead, it is important that he be introduced to the machine and its possibilities, that he know the behavior of materials and how to work them. In his later career he will then be possessed of an intuition that will stand him in good stead when he attempts to design rocket devices or when he is called upon to diagnose the cause of failure of some existing device.

Also in high school it is very important that a strong course in mathematics be pursued, so precious college time will not be wasted in reestablishing what should have been thoroughly absorbed in the high school. Courses in physics and chemistry should be taken, again to establish principles from which departure into more specialized courses can be undertaken in college.

Here, in high school, two very important points must be stressed. First—and this is a problem receiving much discussion today—the high schools of our country must be strengthened, either as a whole or in many centralized locations. It may be necessary to expand and strengthen some high schools and to provide transportation for gifted students who can profit by attending them. It may not be totally a matter of more money to be spent. It may instead come down to somewhat more money, but most of all a penetrating soul-searching in the matter of how we are spending our money today. Certainly the average high school teacher has received inadequate training, not for lack of money spent in the process but for lack of appreciation on the part of the public and of the educators that these teachers, above all, must be the most capable that our society can furnish. Today, there has been too much of the attitude that only a trivial or superficial high school education can be given to the masses, so trivial and superficial teachers will suffice.

The second essential point in high school training for the space age is one that depends almost entirely on the student, with some guidance by parents, friends, and educators. The student must know, very early, what he wants to do, so he can plan every hour of his school career from entry into high school until, some nine to twelve or thirteen years later, his education is complete. This has always been a problem; today too many students enter college and pass through two years or more of scattered courses without knowing really what they wish to do. There must be provided, somewhere along the way, with intelligent advice and counseling, through programs carefully worked out for that specific purpose.

After having passed through the formal high school training, it may be wise for the student to work for a year in an industry, as the author did, to get more of the feeling of how things are made and put together to accomplish specific purposes. There is here also the opportunity to earn money and to know the value of it, and to apply it to the long and expensive college career ahead.

The choice of a college presents a problem. Fortunately, in this country there are many fine ones, and the small liberal arts colleges of a few hundred students must never be underrated. The instructors are, in large measure, dedicated to good teaching, because they are not so obligated to pursue research, as is likely to be the situation in a larger institution. However, in this very point there lies a strong indication that the student who knows that he wishes to become a space engineer should avoid a small college, however good and however convenient to his own home.

He must have access to large laboratories, properly equipped, and to prestige faculty members who are in the midst of current and even future developments and thinking in the field. It may well be that not one institution in the whole country today is equipped to handle the specific kind of training needed. Dr. S. Fred Singer of the University of Maryland, a ranking authority in astronautics, believes that space flight training on the graduate level should be concentrated into centers, rather than in particular colleges or univeristies. He indicates that for forty to fifty students doing graduate work in the field there should be a staff of perhaps ten scientists teaching specific topics. It might be necessary for these students to move from one institution to another to find these specialists; later, their degrees might be granted from two or more institutions jointly.

The author is partial to those institutions that operate on the coöperative basis. In these, the student can, after the first year, spend half his time in the college halls and the other half in industry, to watch and to participate in the manufacture and operation of the very parts he must work with later. Usually coöperative colleges operate on a five-year basis, but the experience in industry is precious, not only for providing money for more education but also because it provides experience and intuition in the crucial formative years, when the student's capacity for absorbing knowledge is, in most cases, at a maximum.

The emphasis must be on specific education—i.e., engineering as opposed to a normal liberal arts specialization in science. And, as in high school, no time must be wasted. The student must be dedicated to the proposition that every hour of his college career is to be devoted to hard study and absorption of difficult material. In these days of a short work week and so much time yet remaining for recreation, it is rather wasteful to pamper the college student when his education is so costly and so precious. The student preparing for a career in science should, in these days, be willing to spend forty or more hours per week in the classroom and laboratory and in the preparation for classes and writing of reports. In addition to this, he should be willing, even anxious, to participate in a great many extra-curricular symposia and colloquia that should be designed to assist him in his thinking.

Certain engineering courses as they are constituted today are of no value in space flight training. For example, civil engineering can be glossed over in connection with surveying and navigation, taught perhaps in an astronomy course, and in the mechanics portion of physics courses. With considerable modification of existing course content, perhaps the most acceptable curriculum is one in aeronautical engineering, with considerable sprinklings of mechanical and electronic engineering courses. It must be realized, of course, that some specialization must be permitted and even encouraged, in the later years of a complete course, because some space flight engineers will be particularly interested in rocket propulsion, others in mechanical design and stabilization of rockets, other in guidance systems, others in telemetering and communications, others in problems of air and food supply and conservation, and so on. As in the training of a mathematician today, or a chemist or a physicist, not all students should take all courses presented, after the first few years.

One line of study that should persist in some form through most of the college curriculum is astronomy, both because that science has been the inspiration for much invention in other fields of science and mathematics and also because in astronomy so many techniques and disciplines of other sciences meet for their finest expressions. Unfortunately, in the past this queen of the sciences has been badly neglected by college administrators, a step-child taught incompetently with little encouragement. As these lines are written, the author knows of no engineering department in the country which requires a good descriptive course in astronomy. Many give astronomy as an elective. Soon, when the demand for space flight engineers becomes very acute, the myopic college administrators will be scrambling and competing for the few teachers qualified in astronomy, and encouraging the preparation of more of them.

Astronomy, and specialized applications of other subjects to astronomy, should be taught through the five years of college, with at least three classes a week and suitable laboratory work to make more vivid the lectures and recitations. In the first year the course is descriptive astronomy, in which the student becomes acquainted with the solar system, the stars, the nebulae, and the galaxies. The emphasis should always be on how we determine what we know, and it will be possible for considerable mathematics and physics to be included in this course because we have presupposed that the student has been properly prepared in high school.

The mathematics of the freshman year should not be devoted, as is so often the case today, to a redoing of the high school mathematics. It should begin with analytic geometry and go on immediately to the cal-

culus. Five hours per week is a minimum requirement here. Mechanical drawing should be undertaken at this time, too, in what might be considered
the laboratory sessions to accompany the mathematics of the classroom. No engineer is of much
value unless he can passably express on paper his interpretation of a theoretical problem, or read, from a
diagram, the significant details of construction and
function.

Strongly specialized courses in physics and chemistry should be taken in this first year. The high
school courses should have sufficed for the surveys
of these fields, and emphasis on mechanics and heat,
optics and electricity and magnetism should be included in physics. The basic specialization in chemistry should be designed for those engineers who
will be interested in problems of rocket propulsion.

There will be those cultural courses such as English, economics, sociology, and other humanities to
be wedged in, somewhere. The English course, in
particular, is of great importance, because too many
engineers in World War II and later were found to
be incapable of communicating with others in re-
lated fields. And in the science curriculum, the teaching of English for engineers should be of a nature
quite different from that designed for the liberal arts
student expecting to go on to novel or poetry writing, or a study of English literature. Scientific English is precise and specific, and students must be

taught to read, write, and speak intelligibly and fluently, if not gracefully. The emphasis must be on the communication and understanding of ideas.

In mathematics in the second year, differential equations and Fourier Series should be pursued. In astronomy, astrophysics and astrometry should be the points of emphasis. The student should spend considerable time at the observatory, not only working with the professional observers but making observations himself, and reducing them. Only a large institution, or one near a large observatory, will have the facilities for this. Here, and in advanced courses in physics and chemistry, the opportunity comes for the understanding of the photographic process and techniques. Spectroscopy, in physics, can follow or accompany introductory hours in the study of atomic structure, and can be applied both in the laboratory and in the observatory. In chemistry, advanced work including the principles of combustion and high temperatures and the behavior of materials should be pursued.

Again there will be requirements in the humanities. Every scientist, including the engineer, should know enough of foreign languages to be able to read original articles written abroad. Especially for graduate work, at least two languages should be available, and it will be better if, somewhere along the way, three of them—French, German, Russian—can be acquired. A high school course is not sufficient and no time in the secondary school should be wasted in this field. In college, the minimum requirement should be five hours per week, intensively taught.

In the third year, atomic energy enters both the physics and chemistry courses. Here the study of the atomic nucleus is emphasized, as contrasted with the orbital elctron arrangements that were the points of interest in spectroscopy and combustion, in the second year. An experimental nuclear pile, either in the university or nearby, is highly desirable for these courses; the student should know from actual examination how a pile works; he should know how it is replenished and how the by-products are extracted and utilized.

In astronomy and mathematics, the practical applications of plane and spherical trigonometry, plane and solid analytic geometry, differential equations, the laws of motion and gravitation all meet in the course called celestial mechanics. The student here learns by actual examples how celestial bodies move and how the astronomer solves for their past, present, and future positions. The equations of motion of a body, even a rocket ship, subject to the laws of central forces will be completely developed and the student will become completely familiar with their applications. This would be a good time, too, for the student to become familiar with the modern methods of calculation by means of programmed computers such as the electronic "brains."

Another foreign language should be pursued and any remaining humanities requirements should be discharged at this time.

In the fourth year, further welding together of mathematics, physics, chemistry, and astronomy materials and techniques should be undertaken, with perhaps the real beginning of the specialization of the field of space flight engineering, according to the student's taste and aptitudes. Another foreign language can be pursued. Many colloquia and symposia should be arranged, so students can watch and take part in free interchange of ideas, both with each other and with experts from the faculty and from other faculties. Every visitor who is engaged in the field should provide an excuse for another colloquium. Some of these informal meetings should be set up specifically for the purpose of encouraging the students to express themselves. Either pre-assigned or spot topics should be handed out, and a minimum presentation demanded and later discussed and graded. This is an excellent way for the student to learn to communicate his own ideas or to paraphrase those of others.

By the end of this fourth year, most of the student's formal training should have been accomplished. We must not lose sight of the fact that, except for the first year, which might well occupy 34 to 36 weeks of the calendar, the student has been spending only 24 or 26 weeks of the year at college, the remainder of the year, except for a brief vacation, in industry. There he will be in daily contact with professional production engineering personnel, working on the very problems that he will undertake when his education is completed. It is desirable, in most instances, that the student spend time in more than one plant or engineering laboratory, to see how different problems are attacked by different engineers with different philosophies. The ideal location for the university or educational center is in a large metropolitan area where many industries are devoted to many aspects of missile work.

An ideal use of half of the fifth year of college work would be to spend it in England, France, Switzerland, Germany, or Russia, to work in engineering industries there. Naturally, students from those other lands would be welcomed here for the same purpose. The infusion of fresh ideas from practices in foreign countries is invaluable in these days when the internationalism of science is so acutely recognized. We need foreign ideas as never before; those in foreign lands need our know-how. The need for use of foreign languages will contribute to understanding of foreign customs and ideals and will contribute to the easing of tensions that so beset the world today. And our greatest mistake would be to assume at this moment that this healthy interchange would not work. The author can almost hear someone saying, "The Russians would never agree to it!"

And, in Russia, someone is probably saying, "The Americans would never agree to it!" We'd better try it, in good faith; we may be surprised at our success.

The remainder of the fifth year might be spent at the White Sands Proving Ground, at Cape Canaveral, or another missile launching or testing station. The student can assist in the preparations for firing of missiles, in tracking procedures by theodolite or radar, and in the interpretation of telemetered information from the vehicle.

A desirable development during the fifth year of the student's education would be complete financing of the cost, including transportation and housing, by government. Critical examination of the student can determine if he then should continue in government service, return for graduate work in space engineering, or prepare, perhaps, to teach others. A minimum period of work in government service might be required in return for this financing of this fifth year of work, and in this period the proper evaluation of the student's capabilities could be made.

At all events, the culmination of five years of a curriculum such as outlined here should be a Bachelor's degree in missile engineering, space flight, or astronautics. But there is much specialized work that can be done beyond this point.

In 1958, the first doctorate in space navigation was granted by the University of California at Los Angeles—the culmination of a long, slow process to institute a graduate degree in this field. Dr. Samuel Herrick, Professor of Astronomy at UCLA and one of the leading authorities in space navigation, laid the foundation for the course in 1939. In 1953 the program was worked out, leading to a Doctor's degree in engineering built around astronautics, the study of navigation in space. Dr. Herrick's pioneering efforts have culminated in such a degree, and approaches to something similar are being made elsewhere.

Dr. Singer, mentioned earlier, has also analyzed the educational problem involved in fitting men for the space travel field, and his recommendations are of extreme interest. He too has graduate students working with him, but so far no formal doctorate in the field is offered by the University of Maryland. He proposes a new type of study leading to an astronautical engineering degree.

Dr. Singer's experience in the field and in industry suggests that insufficient training hampers the men in the field today. Engineers testify that, no matter what their background, they find it necessary to study a great deal more physics and astronomy to keep abreast of the scientific and technical aspects of astronautics. The engineer, instead of holding closely to present-day rocket engines, aerodynamics and electronics, has reached the point where he must possess a basic knowledge of new schemes of propulsion, ion rockets, magnetohydrodynamics, the electromagnetic spectrum, and celestial mechanics.

Instead of squeezing more courses into the already overcrowded curriculum of the engineering student, Dr. Singer proposes graduate work for the engineer. The author believes that, with the carefully planned emphasis that has already been set down here, much of the material can be studied at the undergraduate level; but let us take a closer look at what Dr. Singer proposes.

In the graduate studies following a more or less conventional engineering course, Dr. Singer would have the student well grounded in atomic and nuclear physics, solid state physics, jet propulsion, aerodynamics, heat transfer, and astronomy. Following this, the highly important theoretical work based on the above background would be undertaken. Relativity, quantum mechanics, and statistical mechanics would fill out the curriculum so that the theoretical background for the basic understanding of the applications of nuclear fission and fusion mechanisms to astronautics would be available.

Dr. Singer indicates that with this kind of training the student could tackle successfully such phenomena as ionized gases, whether inisde a thrust chamber of a rocket, in interplanetary space or in the solar atmosphere. He would be able to study the complicated interactions involving the hydrodynamics of an ionized gas and the magnetic fields and electric currents in the gas which would ready him at least in a theoretical sense for the basic understanding of nuclear reactors of the future and their applications to astronautics.

Simultaneously the theoretical approach would be supplemented by practical research, the finest teaching medium for the advanced student. As an example of this novel and ingenious approach at the University of Maryland, a small rocket, the Terrapin, has been developed in coöperation with Republic Aviation. This is a small rocket, weighing only 100 pounds, but very useful in astronautics as an upper-atmosphere exploration device. These rockets can reach remarkable altitudes if properly designed for a light payload. Because they are so inexpensive and so easily launched, they are eminently suited to a university research and development project.

The Terrapin rocket costs about $2000. If a still less expensive rocket is indicated, the Oriole, which also has a 100-mile ceiling, and which Dr. Singer and his University of Maryland group can build, comes to about $500. Rockets for really high altitudes are more expensive, of course; the Curlybird, which can reach an altitude of from 600 to 1000 miles, costs about $4000.

If there is a large number of graduate students involved in such a project, a university can develop rockets by sub-contracting that can climb to 10,000 miles, at a cost of about $50,000. We should realize that in most instances the research branches of the armed services will underwrite the costs of these probes; such programs have great merit—not only in advancing our knowledge of the atmosphere but also in training future space flight engineers. Dr. Singer points out that such research projects, rather than interfering with already-established missile programs, enhance them by providing data important to missile designers.

With this type of small rocket, graduate students can undertake the instrumentation, programming, and launching as a research project. Educationally, this type of practical program is invaluable. Not only does the student gain experience in rocket propulsion and aerodynamical design, but he also becomes acquainted with many practical aspects of rocket storage, handling, launching, telemetering techniques, and recovery. He becomes familiar with the miniaturization of electronic equipment, with transistors and magnetic cores and other phases and devices of control, telemetering, and radio applications in the missile field. The upper-atmosphere information and the knowledge of properties of extra-terrestrial radiations gleaned by such rockets will give the student important insight into astrophysics and the types of problems which must be resolved in the age of astronautics.

Educators have long agreed that the best way to

acquire an education is to learn by doing, and in science this means laboratory and field research under proper supervision and guidance. Graduate students can choose as research projects from the following: The intensity and variation of solar ultraviolet and X-rays, the nature and density of interplanetary dust, the composition and altitude and latitude variations of the primary cosmic rays, the nature and intensity of the auroral particles, the measurement of electric current systems in the ionosphere and outer atmosphere, the density and temperature of the outer atmosphere.

When a student has completed a course as outlined above, from the intensive high school preparation through the undergraduate study and industrial experience, at last into graduate work and research, he should be fully qualified to undertake any mission in the missile field and successfully pursue it to a conclusion. Not only will he be an expert in this field, however; we can well consider him a truly educated expert in the whole field of the exact sciences.

Index